# Longman Practice Exam Papers

# A-level Chemistry

**Michael C Cox**
**Philip J Barratt**

**Series editors:**

**Geoff Black and Stuart Wall**

## Titles available for A-Level

Biology

Business Studies

Chemistry

Physics

Psychology

Pure Mathematics and Mechanics

Pure Mathematics and Statistics

Addison Wesley Longman Limited
Edinburgh Gate, Harlow
Essex CM20 2JE, England
*and Associated Companies throughout the World*

First published 1999

ISBN 0-582-36921-5

**British Library Cataloguing in Publication Data**
A catalogue record for this book is available from the British Library

Set in Times 11/13 and Gill Sans by 38

Printed in Singapore through Addison Wesley Longman China Ltd, Hong Kong

# Contents

# Editors' preface

**Longman Practice Exam Papers** are written by experienced A-level examiners and teachers. They will provide you with an ideal opportunity to practise under exam-type conditions before your actual school or college mocks or before the A-level examination itself. As well as becoming familiar with the vital skill of pacing yourself through a whole exam paper, you can check your answers against examiner solutions and mark schemes to assess the level you have reached.

**Longman Practice Exam Papers** can be used alongside *Longman A-level Study Guides* and *Longman Exam Practice Kits* to provide a comprehensive range of home study support as you prepare to take your A-level in each subject covered.

# Acknowledgements

Once more we are grateful to the Publishers, Addison Wesley Longman, and to the series editors, Geoff Black and Stuart Wall, for inviting us to write this book and thereby giving us another opportunity to help students achieve their potential of really good grades in chemistry.

We should also like to thank again our many professional colleagues for sharing their expertise with us. We are especially grateful to our colleague of long-standing, Dr Margaret Cross, for giving us the benefit of her many years of experience as Chief Examiner in Chemistry for another major board. Her advice and constructive comments on our question papers and mark schemes were invaluable. Needless to say, if there are any mistakes or ambiguities in this book, it is entirely our own fault.

Above all we wish to thank our wives, Maureen and Maureen, for their continuing love, patience and support yet again!

Michael Cox
Philip Barratt

# Introduction

As a good student you know you must prepare thoroughly to achieve really good grades in your examinations. To help you improve your exam performance, you will find in this book

- five chemistry papers to be tackled under exam conditions
- complete mark schemes with which to check your answers
- tips and information from examiners.

## Timing of the practice papers

All five structured papers are A-level/H-grade and suitable for modular assessment or for end-of-course assessment. The first four are 60-minute papers worth 60 marks each. Papers 1 and 2 are modules biased towards advanced supplementary work. You could combine either chemistry paper with Paper 3 or 4 to make a 2-hour exam paper. Paper 5 is a 90-minute synoptic paper but worth only 85 marks because we have included a comprehension exercise and allowed you 5 minutes for reading the passage. Remember the general rule:

- one minute of exam time is worth at least one mark.

## What will you need?

For Papers 1 to 4 you will write your answers in the spaces provided in this book but you will need some paper to write your answers to Paper 5. What else will you need?

As examiners we have to test your knowledge and understanding of the fundamental facts, patterns, principles and theories of chemistry. We also have to test your ability to

- draw and clearly label diagrams
- write and balance equations
- do calculations (pH, $\Delta H$, $K_c$, $E_a$, etc.)
- predict the feasibility of reactions
- deduce organic structures.

So you will need to provide yourself with pens, pencils, a ruler, an eraser and a calculator. Different examination boards have different regulations about calculators. For example, you may not be allowed to take the instruction manual into the examination room. If your calculator is programmable, you may have to clear the memory. As a good student, you will check the regulations in your own copy of the board's syllabus.

You should also check your syllabus and regulations to see if you are required to supply your own data book in the examination. Some boards may provide essential data in the question paper, or separately in the form of a booklet. *For these practice papers, we have given you the essential physical constants with the relevant question and a periodic table containing relative atomic masses on page vi.*

## Further help and guidance

In these five practice papers we cover the essential chemistry common to all the examination board syllabuses. You will find quick revision summaries of this essential chemistry in the *Longman Exam Practice Kit*, which was designed for you to practise answering questions individually set on each of the seven core chemistry topics: structure and bonding, energetics, kinetics, chemical equilibria, electrochemistry and redox, the periodic table and organic chemistry. You will find an analysis of the various examination syllabuses in the *Longman Study Guide*. All three books were designed to help you to help yourself. So turn over now to see how you can help yourself to make the most of these practice papers.

# How to use this book

**Treat these practice papers seriously.** Take the advice offered in the *Longman Exam Practice Kit*: persuade a relative or friend to supervise your examination by starting you off, keeping an eye on you and telling you when to stop. Better still, why not co-operate with another student.

- Set yourselves the same practice paper.
- Work separately but under the same exam conditions.
- When the time is up, swap and mark each other's papers.
- Check your marking and discuss each other's mistakes.

**Remember that time is your enemy.** Keep your eye on it. Do not spend too much time on one question and not enough time on another. Time lost can rarely be recovered. If you run out of time towards the end of a paper, write your answers in note form. However, bear in mind that examiners give credit for the quality of your language, including clarity of expression, structure, grammar, punctuation and spelling.

**Mark your answers carefully.** Put each mark in the right-hand margin. Note that for some questions where there could be more than one correct answer, we indicate if possible other valid answers in our mark schemes. Note also that where there is only one correct answer, there may still be more than one way of expressing it. *In this book your mark schemes include the full answers we should expect and require an A-grade candidate to write down.* In practice, we refer to an abbreviated form of these schemes when marking your papers. Where necessary we have underlined the words that would form our working mark scheme.

**Correct any mistakes.** As stated in our *Longman Exam Practice Kit*, answering questions is important but only half the task. Studying our mark schemes, thinking about your mistakes and acting on our tips will be time very well spent. If any of your answers are wrong, make sure you understand not only why they are wrong, but also what the correct answer should be and why.

Good luck from both of us.

MCC & PJB

# Periodic table

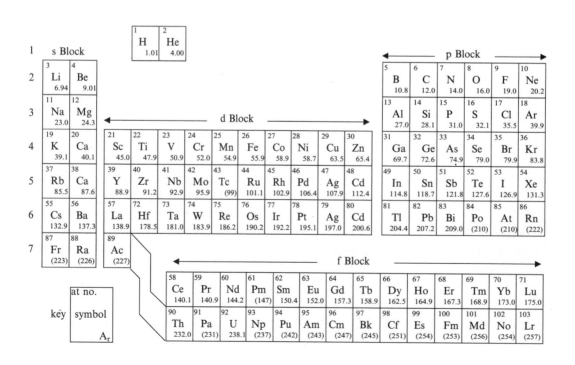

# Longman
# Examination Board

**General Certificate of Education**

**Chemistry**

**Paper 1 (Module)**

**Time: 60 minutes**

| Question number | Mark |
|---|---|
| 1. | |
| 2. | |
| 3. | |
| 4. | |
| **Total Mark** | |

**Instructions**

■ Attempt **all** the questions.

■ Write your answers in the spaces provided.

■ Use a blue or black ink pen or ball-point.

**Information for candidates**

■ The number of marks for each question or part-question is given in brackets.

■ The total mark for each question is given at the end of each question.

■ The periodic table is printed on page vi and contains all relative atomic masses.

■ **The maximum mark for this paper is 60.**

---

*Leave margin blank*

1.  (a)  (i)  Distinguish between the terms *mass number* and *relative atomic mass*.

    ...................................................................................................................

    ...................................................................................................................

    ...................................................................................................................

    ...................................................................................................................

    **(2 marks)**

    (ii)  State the number of protons, neutrons and electrons in an ion of sodium, $^{22}Na^+$.

    ...................................................................................................................

    **(1 mark)**

    (b)  A normal isotopic mixture of bromine contains equal numbers of $^{79}Br$ and $^{81}Br$ atoms.

    (i)  State the relative atomic mass of bromine.

    ...................................................................................................................

    **(1 mark)**

    **Turn over**

    1

(ii) On the axes below draw the mass spectrum for elemental bromine in the region of the molecular ion, $Br_2^+$. Mark clearly the ratio of peak heights and label the mass/charge ratio for each peak.

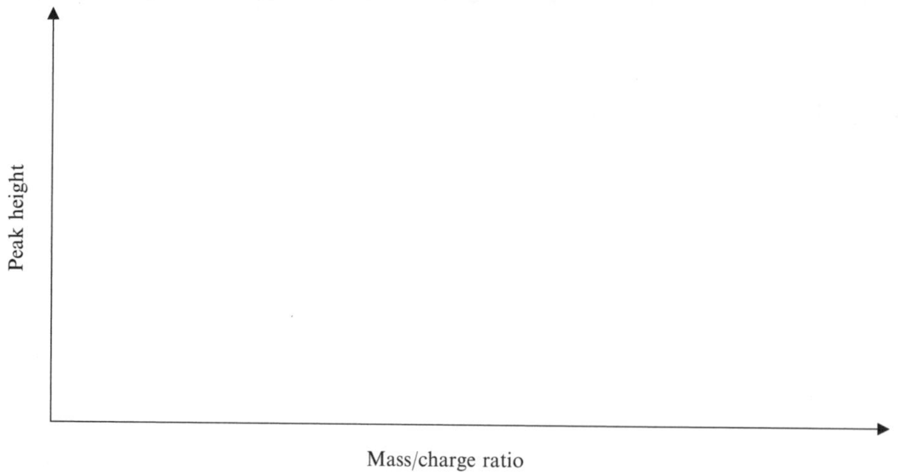

Peak height

Mass/charge ratio

**(2 marks)**

(c) (i) Show clearly by dot and cross diagrams the formation of sodium chloride from sodium and chlorine.

**(1 mark)**

(ii) Show clearly by dot and cross diagrams the formation of ammonia from nitrogen and hydrogen.

**(1 mark)**

(iii) By reference to sodium chloride and ammonia, name the type of bonding involved in **each** compound and explain how **two** physical properties of the compounds differ because of the difference in bonding.

..............................................................................................................................

..............................................................................................................................

..............................................................................................................................

..............................................................................................................................

**(4 marks)**

**Total: 12 marks**

**2.** (a) Describe qualitatively what happens when a solid is heated until it becomes a gas.

..............................................................................................................................

..............................................................................................................................

..............................................................................................................................

..............................................................................................................................

**(3 marks)**

(b) (i) State Hess's law.

..............................................................................................................................

..............................................................................................................................

**(1 mark)**

(ii) Ethyne, $C_2H_2$, is a gas that burns readily in oxygen to form carbon dioxide and water.

$$2C_2H_2(g) + 5O_2(g) \rightarrow 4CO_2(g) + 2H_2O(l)$$

Use the following standard enthalpy changes of combustion to determine the standard enthalpy change of formation, $\Delta H_f^\ominus$, of ethyne.

| Substance | Standard enthalpy change of combustion/kJ mol$^{-1}$ |
|---|---|
| Hydrogen, $H_2(g)$ | $-286$ |
| Carbon, $C(s)$ | $-394$ |
| Ethyne, $C_2H_2(g)$ | $-1299$ |

**(3 marks)**

(c) (i) Predict the enthalpy change of combustion of gaseous ethanol, $C_2H_5OH$, using the following equation and bond energies.

$$C_2H_5OH(g) + 3O_2(g) \rightarrow 2CO_2(g) + 3H_2O(g)$$

| Bond | Bond energy | Bond | Bond energy |
|---|---|---|---|
| C–H | 413 | O–H | 464 |
| C–C | 347 | O=O | 498 |
| C=O ($CO_2$) | 805 | C–O | 358 |

..............................................................................................................................

..............................................................................................................................

..............................................................................................................................

**(3 marks)**

**Turn over**

(ii) Suggest why there is a small difference between the value predicted in (c)(i) above and the experimental value.

...................................................................................................................................

...................................................................................................................................

**(1 mark)**

(d) State **two** factors that determine whether an ionic solid dissolves in water exothermically or endothermically.

...................................................................................................................................

...................................................................................................................................

**(2 marks)**

**Total: 13 marks**

**3.** (a) On the axes below sketch

(i) the variation of the logarithm of the eleven ionisation energies of the electrons in a sodium atom against the number of the electron removed;

Log IE

Number of the electron removed

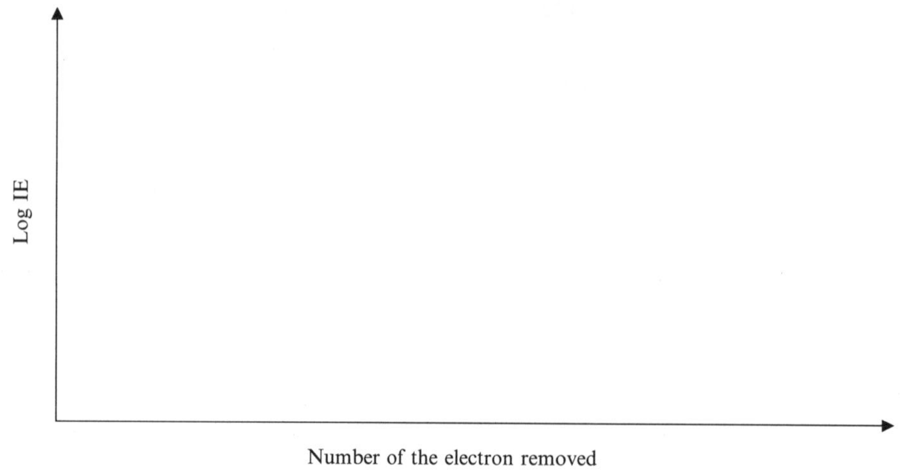

**(2 marks)**

(ii) the variation of molar first ionisation energy for the elements hydrogen to calcium (atomic numbers 1 to 20).

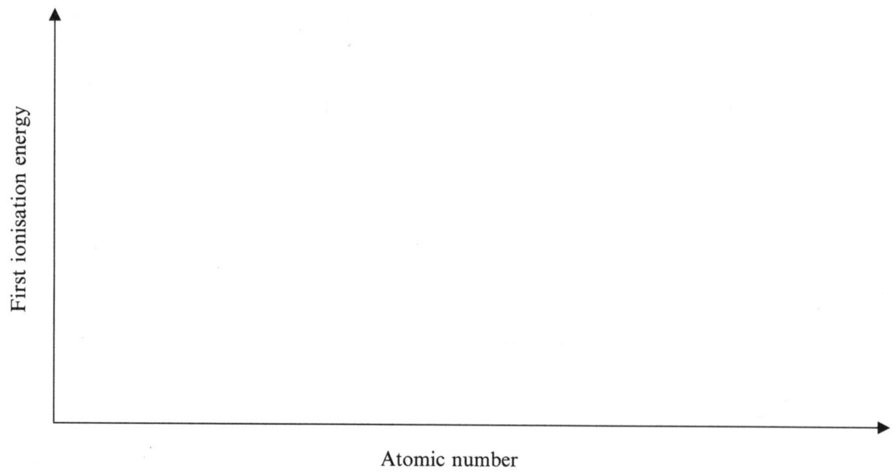

First ionisation energy

Atomic number

**(3 marks)**

(b) Describe how **each** of the following elements reacts with water. Include in each answer what would be observed and a balanced chemical equation for the reaction.

    (i)   sodium

       **Observations** ...........................................................................................

       **Equation** ...............................................................................................

                                                                              **(2 marks)**

    (ii)  chlorine.

       **Observations** ...........................................................................................

       **Equation** ...............................................................................................

                                                                               **(2 marks)**

(c) From the oxides of the elements in the period from sodium to argon give the name **and** formula of:

    (i)   an amphoteric oxide ...................................................... **(1 mark)**

    (ii)  a giant covalent oxide ..............................................................

                                                                               **(1 mark)**

(d) In the periodic table the first element in a Group is said to be atypical because some of its chemical properties are different from those of the rest of its Group. Illustrate this statement with **two** examples of your own choice from Groups 1 and 7. For each example, state both the typical and atypical chemical property.

    **Example 1**

    ..........................................................................................................

    ..........................................................................................................

    **Example 2**

    ..........................................................................................................

    ..........................................................................................................

                                                                            **(4 marks)**

                                                          **Total: 15 marks**

4. (a) Explain **each** of the following terms.

    (i)   Heterolytic fission of a covalent bond

       ..........................................................................................

       ..........................................................................................

                                                                             **(2 marks)**

    (ii)  Nucleophile.

       ..........................................................................................

       ..........................................................................................

                                                                             **(2 marks)**

(b) (i) Classify the type of mechanism for the reaction of ethene with hydrogen bromide.

       ..........................................................................................

                                                                             **(1 mark)**

**Turn over**

*Leave margin blank*

(ii) Give the reaction mechanism in (b)(i).

**(3 marks)**

(iii) Describe what would be observed on passing ethene into a mixture of aqueous bromine and aqueous sodium chloride.

....................................................................................................................

**(1 mark)**

(iv) Name **two** possible organic compounds, other than 1,2-dibromoethane, produced in (b)(iii) and discuss briefly why they are formed.

....................................................................................................................

....................................................................................................................

....................................................................................................................

....................................................................................................................

....................................................................................................................

**(3 marks)**

(c) State the reagents and conditions required to convert 1-bromobutane into

   (i) butan-1-ol;

....................................................................................................................

**(2 marks)**

  (ii) pentanenitrile.

....................................................................................................................

**(2 marks)**

(iii) Classify the type of mechanism for the reaction in (c)(i).

....................................................................................................................

**(1 mark)**

(iv) Give the reaction mechanism in (c)(iii).

**(3 marks)**

**Total: 20 marks**

**End of Paper 1**

# Longman
# Examination Board

## General Certificate of Education

## Chemistry

## Paper 2 (Module)

**Time: 60 minutes**

| Question number | Mark |
|---|---|
| 1. | |
| 2. | |
| 3. | |
| 4. | |
| 5. | |
| Total Mark | |

Margin to be used by examiners to record their marks and the totals

### Instructions

■ Attempt **all** the questions.

■ Write your answers in the spaces provided.

■ Use a blue or black ink pen or ball-point.

### Information for candidates

■ The number of marks for each question or part-question is given in brackets.

■ The total mark for each question is given at the end of each question.

■ The periodic table is printed on page vi and contains all relative atomic masses.

■ **The maximum mark for this paper is 60.**

---

1. (a) Explain the meaning of the term *dynamic equilibrium*.

........................................................................................................................

........................................................................................................................

*Leave margin blank*

**(1 mark)**

(b) Ethanol can be manufactured by the direct hydration of ethene.

$$C_2H_4(g) + H_2O(g) \rightleftharpoons C_2H_5OH(g) \qquad \Delta H = -46\,\text{kJ}\,\text{mol}^{-1}$$

(i) Write an expression for the equilibrium constant $K_p$, for this reaction.



**(1 mark)**

(ii) State and explain how the amount of ethanol in the equilibrium mixture would change with an increase in the temperature and total pressure of the mixture.

**Temperature** ...............................................................................................

........................................................................................................................

........................................................................................................................

**(2 marks)**

**Turn over**

Total pressure ...................................................................................................

............................................................................................................................

............................................................................................................................

**(2 marks)**

(iii) In the manufacturing process the temperature is about 570 K and the total pressure is between 60 and 70 atmospheres. Suggest what might happen to the ethene at a very much higher total pressure.

............................................................................................................................

**(1 mark)**

(iv) The following table shows the equilibrium partial pressures at a given temperature.

| Compound | Partial pressure/atmospheres |
|----------|------------------------------|
| Ethene | 31 |
| Steam | 31 |
| Ethanol | 3 |

Calculate the value of the equilibrium constant, $K_p$, at this given temperature.

............................................................................................................................

............................................................................................................................

**(2 marks)**

(v) On the basis of the data in (b)(iv), suggest **two** important practical requirements for obtaining a good yield when manufacturing ethanol by this method.

............................................................................................................................

............................................................................................................................

**(2 marks)**

(c) When ethanol is oxidised by aqueous sodium dichromate(VI) and aqueous sulphuric acid, ethanoic acid, $CH_3COOH$, a weak organic acid is formed.

(i) State what is meant by the term *weak acid*.

............................................................................................................................

............................................................................................................................

**(1 mark)**

(ii) The value of $pK_a$ for ethanoic acid at 298 K is 4.74. Calculate the pH value for an aqueous solution of ethanoic acid of concentration $0.055 \, mol \, dm^{-3}$ at 298 K.

............................................................................................................................

............................................................................................................................

............................................................................................................................

**(2 marks)**

(iii) Explain why an aqueous mixture of sodium ethanoate and ethanoic acid behaves as a buffer solution. Chemical equations are **not** required.

...........................................................................................................................

...........................................................................................................................

...........................................................................................................................

...........................................................................................................................

**(3 marks)**

**Total: 17 marks**

**2.** (a) (i) Give the reagents and conditions for the conversion of benzene to nitrobenzene.

...........................................................................................................................

...........................................................................................................................

**(2 marks)**

(ii) Classify the reaction mechanism in (a)(i).

...........................................................................................................................

**(1 mark)**

(iii) Show the mechanism by which benzene is converted to nitrobenzene.

**(3 marks)**

(b) (i) When nitrobenzene is reduced, phenylamine is formed. Give the formula of phenylamine.

...........................................................................................................................

**(1 mark)**

(ii) State the reagents and conditions required to convert phenylamine to aqueous benzenediazonium chloride.

...........................................................................................................................

...........................................................................................................................

**(2 marks)**

(iii) Methyl orange, a dye with the following structure, may be prepared by a coupling reaction between N:N-dimethyl benzene and a diazonium compound.

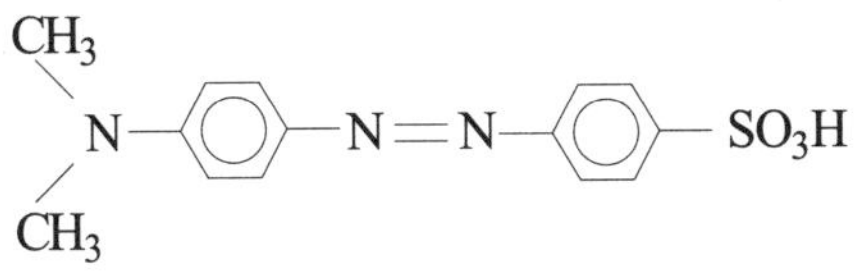

Draw the structures of two molecules that form methyl orange by a coupling reaction.

**(2 marks)**

**Total: 11 marks**

**Turn over**

3. (a) (i) Give **two** general chemical characteristics of transition elements.

......................................................................................................

......................................................................................................

......................................................................................................

......................................................................................................

**(2 marks)**

(ii) Write the ground state electronic configurations in terms of s, p and d electrons for the manganese(II) ion, **Mn$^{2+}$** and for the chromium atom, **Cr**.

......................................................................................................

......................................................................................................

**(2 marks)**

(iii) Why should zinc, cadmium and mercury not be classed as transition metals?

......................................................................................................

......................................................................................................

**(1 mark)**

(b) Give the oxidation states of the transition element in **each** of the following.

(i) $VO_3^-$  ............  **(1 mark)**

(ii) $MnO_4^{2-}$  ............  **(1 mark)**

(iii) Write the formula of the anion in sodium chromate(VI)  ............  **(1 mark)**

(iv) State and explain, with the help of a balanced **ionic** equation, the change in colour when dilute sulphuric acid is added to aqueous sodium chromate(VI).

......................................................................................................

......................................................................................................

**(2 marks)**

(c) (i) State the shape of the hexaaquairon(III) ion.

......................................................................................................

**(1 mark)**

(ii) State **one** reagent which will oxidise aqueous iron(II) ions and write an **ionic** equation for the reaction.

......................................................................................................

......................................................................................................

**(2 marks)**

**Total: 13 marks**

*Leave margin blank*

**4.** An organic compound, **X**, contains carbon, hydrogen and oxygen only.

Its simplified mass spectrum is

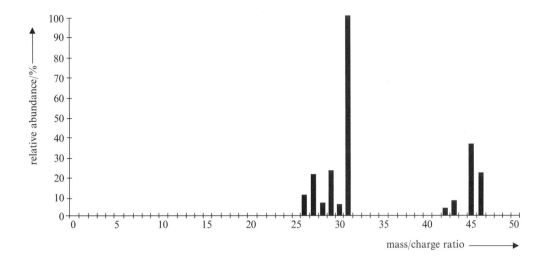

Its low resolution NMR spectrum shows three distinct absorptions with the areas under the peaks in the ratio $3:2:1$.

Its infrared spectrum is

Infrared absorption tables give the following information.

| Bond | Wavenumber/cm$^{-1}$ |
|---|---|
| O−H stretch (hydrogen bonding) | 3600–3500 broad |
| C=O | 1740–1700 |
| C−O stretch | 1200–1050 |

**Turn over**

(a) From the mass spectrum, give

   (i) the mass/charge ratio for the molecular ion peak .......................................................

   **(1 mark)**

   (ii) **one** ion which could produce the peak at mass/charge ratio 29 ...........................

   **(1 mark)**

   (iii) **one** ion which could produce the peak at mass/charge ratio 45 ...........................

   **(1 mark)**

(b) From the IR absorption spectrum and table of related data, give the name of the most likely oxygen-containing functional group in this compound, **X**.

   .................................................................................................................................

   **(1 mark)**

(c) Suggest the name of this compound, **X**, and explain the NMR data in relation to its molecular structure.

   .................................................................................................................................

   .................................................................................................................................

   .................................................................................................................................

   .................................................................................................................................

   .................................................................................................................................

   **(4 marks)**

(d) Name **two** techniques that enable the separation of a mixture of chemically similar organic compounds.

   .................................................................................................................................

   .................................................................................................................................

   **(2 marks)**

   **Total: 10 marks**

5. (a) (i) State the names of **two** different forms of carbon having giant covalent structures.

   .................................................................................................................................

   .................................................................................................................................

   **(2 marks)**

   (ii) Explain, in terms of structure, **two** differences in the physical properties of these forms.

   .................................................................................................................................

   .................................................................................................................................

   .................................................................................................................................

   .................................................................................................................................

   **(3 marks)**

(b) Fullerene, $C_{60}$, is another form of carbon existing as $C_{60}$ molecules in which five and six membered rings of carbon atoms make up a football-like structure.

*Leave margin blank*

(i) Alkali metals such as caesium react with fullerene. Use your knowledge of the s-block elements to show that the following equation represents a redox reaction.

$$3Cs + C_{60} \rightarrow Cs_3C_{60}$$

..............................................................................................................

..............................................................................................................

..............................................................................................................

**(2 marks)**

(ii) Fullerene can be dissolved in benzene and by evaporating the solvent, crystals with the formula $C_{60}.nC_6H_6$ can be grown. Calculate the value of $n$ assuming that the crystals have a molar mass of $1032\,g\,mol^{-1}$ and contain 97.65% carbon by mass.

..............................................................................................................

..............................................................................................................

..............................................................................................................

..............................................................................................................

..............................................................................................................

**(2 marks)**

**Total: 9 marks**

**End of Paper 2**

# Longman Examination Board

## General Certificate of Education

## Chemistry

## Paper 3 (Module)

**Time: 60 minutes**

| Question number | Mark |
|---|---|
| 1. | |
| 2. | |
| 3. | |
| 4. | |
| Total Mark | |

**Instructions**

- Attempt **all** the questions.
- Write your answers in the spaces provided.
- Use a blue or black ink pen or ball-point.

**Information for candidates**

- The number of marks for each question or part-question is given in brackets.
- The total mark for each question is given at the end of each question.
- The periodic table is printed on page vi and contains all relative atomic masses.
- **The maximum mark for this paper is 60.**

---

1. (a) The drug ibuprofen has the following structural formula.

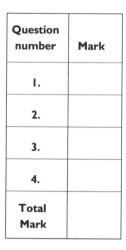

*Leave margin blank*

    (i) State, giving a reason, the type of stereoisomerism shown by this compound.

............................................................................................

............................................................................................

**(2 marks)**

    (ii) Ibuprofen can be formed from a nitrile by hydrolysis with boiling aqueous hydrochloric acid. Draw the structure of the nitrile.

**(1 mark)**

(b) Sorbic acid and its potassium salt are food preservatives. Sorbic acid shows geometrical isomerism and has the following structure.

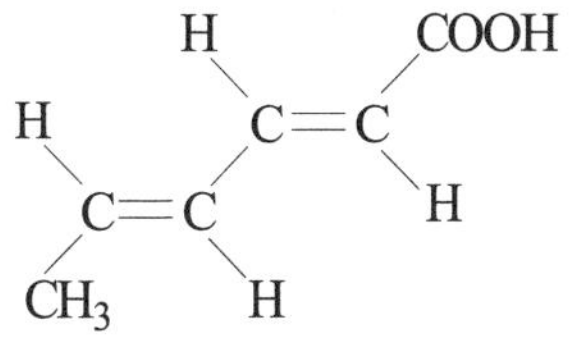

$$\begin{array}{c} H \quad\quad COOH \\ C=C \\ H \quad\quad\quad H \\ C=C \\ CH_3 \quad H \end{array}$$

(i) Including the sorbic acid structure above, how many geometrical isomers are there?

.......................................................................................................................

**(1 mark)**

(ii) Draw **two** of the geometrical isomers excluding the sorbic acid structure shown above.

**(2 marks)**

(iii) State the name of the compound produced by catalytic hydrogenation of sorbic acid.

.......................................................................................................................

**(1 mark)**

(c) Alanine is an $\alpha$-amino acid with molecular formula $C_3H_7NO_2$.

(i) Draw the **two** optical isomers of alanine.

**(2 marks)**

(ii) Write the structural formulae of **two different** dipeptide molecules that may be formed from one molecule of alanine and one molecule of glycine (aminoethanoic acid).

**(2 marks)**

(d) Two compounds **A** and **B** have the same molecular formula, $C_4H_8O$. Ammoniacal silver nitrate solution (Tollen's reagent) reacts with **A** but not **B**. Sodium tetrahydrido-borate(III) reacts with both compounds but only **B** gives a compound **C** which can exist as optical isomers. Identify **A**, **B** and **C**, giving your reasoning.

.......................................................................................................................

.......................................................................................................................

.......................................................................................................................

.......................................................................................................................

.......................................................................................................................

.......................................................................................................................

**(6 marks)**

**Total: 17 marks**

**Turn over**

**2.** (a) Give the ground state electronic configuration of **each** of the following. (The electronic structure of a zinc atom is shown as an example.)

3d orbitals                4s

Zn | Argon core | ↑↓ | ↑↓ | ↑↓ | ↑↓ | ↑↓ |   ↑↓

$Fe^{3+}$ | Argon core |

$V^{2+}$ | Argon core |

Cu | Argon core |

**(3 marks)**

(b) For the complex anion $CoCl_4^{2-}$, state

(i) the oxidation number of the cobalt ......................................................... **(1 mark)**

(ii) the shape of the complex anion. ......................................................... **(1 mark)**

(c) Two compounds, **A** and **B**, have the formula $Co(NH_3)_4Cl_3$ and two compounds, **C** and **D**, have the formulae $Co(NH_3)_5Cl_3$ and $Co(NH_3)_6Cl_3$ respectively. In all four compounds the oxidation state of cobalt is +3. When separate aqueous solutions of **A**, **B**, **C** and **D**, each containing 0.01 mole of the compound, are treated with dilute nitric acid and excess silver nitrate, they produce respectively 0.01, 0.01, 0.02 and 0.03 mol of silver chloride. Draw structures for the cations in **A**, **B**, **C** and **D**.

**cation A**                **cation B**

**cation C**                **cation D**

**(4 marks)**

(d) The reaction scheme below involves some of the chemistry of the aqueous copper(II) ion.

(i) Give the formula of the aqueous copper(II) ion present in aqueous copper(II) sulphate.

.......................................................................................................................................

**(1 mark)**

(ii) Give the formula and shape of the copper-containing cation in **X**.

.......................................................................................................................................

**(2 marks)**

(iii) Give the name and formula of the predominant copper species in **Y**.

.......................................................................................................................................

.......................................................................................................................................

.......................................................................................................................................

**(2 marks)**

(iv) Write a balanced equation for the reaction of aqueous copper(II) sulphate with aqueous potassium iodide.

.......................................................................................................................................

**(1 mark)**

**Total: 15 marks**

**3.** (a) Define the term *standard electrode potential of a metal*.

.......................................................................................................................................

.......................................................................................................................................

.......................................................................................................................................

.......................................................................................................................................

.......................................................................................................................................

**(2 marks)**

**Turn over**

(b) The diagram below shows two half-cells connected by a salt bridge.

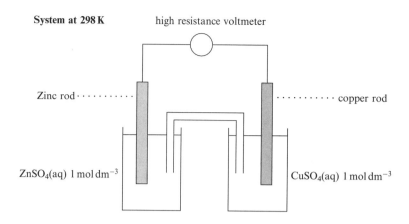

**System at 298 K**      high resistance voltmeter

Zinc rod · · · · · · · · · ·     · · · · · · · · · · copper rod

$ZnSO_4(aq)$ 1 mol dm$^{-3}$       $CuSO_4(aq)$ 1 mol dm$^{-3}$

(i) Name a suitable material for the salt bridge.

..................................................................................................................

**(1 mark)**

(ii) Use the following standard electrode potentials of copper and zinc to calculate the reading on the voltmeter.

$$Zn^{2+}(aq) + 2e^- \rightleftharpoons Zn(s); \quad E^\ominus = -0.76 \text{ volts}$$

$$Cu^{2+}(aq) + 2e^- \rightleftharpoons Cu(s); \quad E^\ominus = +0.34 \text{ volts}$$

..................................................................................................................

**(1 mark)**

(iii) Write a cell diagram for the system represented in the above apparatus diagram.

..................................................................................................................

**(1 mark)**

(iv) When the zinc half-cell is replaced by a silver rod dipping into aqueous silver nitrate of concentration 1.0 mol dm$^{-3}$, the voltmeter reading is 0.46 V.

State the standard electrode potential for $Ag^+(aq) + e^- \rightleftharpoons Ag(s)$.

..................................................................................................................

**(1 mark)**

(v) The silver and copper rods are set up as described in (a)(iv) and connected together externally with a wire. In which direction would electrons flow in the wire?

..................................................................................................................

**(1 mark)**

(c)  The table below shows standard redox data for a number of systems.

| Redox system | $E^{\ominus}/V$ |
|---|---|
| $MnO_4^-(aq) + 8H^+(aq) + 5e^- \rightleftharpoons Mn^{2+}(aq) + 4H_2O(l)$ | +1.51 |
| $Cr_2O_7^{2-}(aq) + 14H^+(aq) + 6e^- \rightleftharpoons 2Cr^{3+}(aq) + 7H_2O(l)$ | +1.33 |
| $VO_2^+(aq) + 2H^+(aq) + e^- \rightleftharpoons VO^{2+}(aq) + H_2O(l)$ | +1.00 |
| $Fe^{3+}(aq) + e^- \rightleftharpoons Fe^{2+}(aq)$ | +0.77 |
| $I_2(aq) + 2e^- \rightleftharpoons 2I^-(aq)$ | +0.54 |

(i)  How many moles of iodine, $I_2(aq)$, could be produced by reacting excess potassium iodide with 0.10 mol of aqueous dichromate(VI), $Cr_2O_7^{2-}(aq)$, in acid solution?

......................................................................................................................................

**(1 mark)**

(ii)  Deduce which species could reduce aqueous dioxovanadium(V) ions.

......................................................................................................................................

......................................................................................................................................

......................................................................................................................................

**(2 marks)**

(iii)  $VO_2^+(aq)$ is yellow and $VO^{2+}(aq)$ is blue. State what you would expect to **observe** if acidified aqueous potassium manganate(VII) were added dropwise to an acidified aqueous solution of vanadium(IV) sulphate until no further change is observed.

......................................................................................................................................

......................................................................................................................................

......................................................................................................................................

......................................................................................................................................

**(3 marks)**

(iv)  One 500 mg iron tablet prescribed for pregnancy was dissolved in aqueous sulphuric acid and the solution made up to 250 cm³ with distilled water in a volumetric flask. 25.0 cm³ of the resulting iron(II) sulphate solution needed 19.1 cm³ of aqueous potassium manganate(VII) of concentration 0.00188 mol dm⁻³ when titrated in the presence of excess sulphuric acid. Calculate the mass of iron in the tablet.

......................................................................................................................................

......................................................................................................................................

......................................................................................................................................

......................................................................................................................................

**(4 marks)**

**Total: 17 marks**

$E^{\ominus}$ **Turn over**

**4.** The data below refer to the reaction represented by the equation

$$NO(g) + Cl_2(g) \rightarrow NOCl(g) + Cl(g)$$

| Concentration of $Cl_2$ /mol dm$^{-3}$ | Concentration of NO /mol dm$^{-3}$ | Rate of reaction /arbitrary units |
|---|---|---|
| 0.002 | 0.002 | 1 |
| 0.002 | 0.004 | 2 |
| 0.001 | 0.002 | 0.5 |

In the Arrhenius equation, $k = A\,e^{-E_a/RT}$, applied to the above reaction, the values of the pre-exponential term, the activation energy and the gas constant are $A = 4.0 \times 10^9\,mol^{-1}\,dm^3\,s^{-1}$, $E_a = 85\,kJ\,mol^{-1}$ and $R = 8.31\,J\,K^{-1}\,mol^{-1}$ respectively.

(a) (i) Write the rate equation for the reaction.

...................................................................................................................

...................................................................................................................

**(1 mark)**

(ii) With reference to the equation in (a)(i) above, explain the term *order of reaction*.

...................................................................................................................

**(1 mark)**

(b) (i) Calculate the value of the rate constant, $k$, for the reaction at 600 K.

...................................................................................................................

...................................................................................................................

**(1 mark)**

(ii) Explain how the activation energy influences the rate of a reaction.

...................................................................................................................

**(1 mark)**

(c) (i) Suggest a mechanism for the reaction that is consistent with the above data.

...................................................................................................................

...................................................................................................................

**(1 mark)**

(ii) State what is meant by the term *rate determining step* and identify clearly this step in the mechanism in (c)(i) above.

...................................................................................................................

...................................................................................................................

**(2 marks)**

(d) The thermal decomposition of gaseous dinitrogen pentoxide is a first order reaction represented by the following stoichiometric equation.

$$2N_2O_5(g) \rightarrow 4NO_2(g) + O_2(g)$$

(i) Suggest an experimental method for following the progress of this reaction and explain why the method should work.

.......................................................................................................................

.......................................................................................................................

.......................................................................................................................

**(2 marks)**

(ii) Sketch a graph to show how the rate of decomposition of the gaseous dinitrogen pentoxide would vary with the partial pressure of the gas.

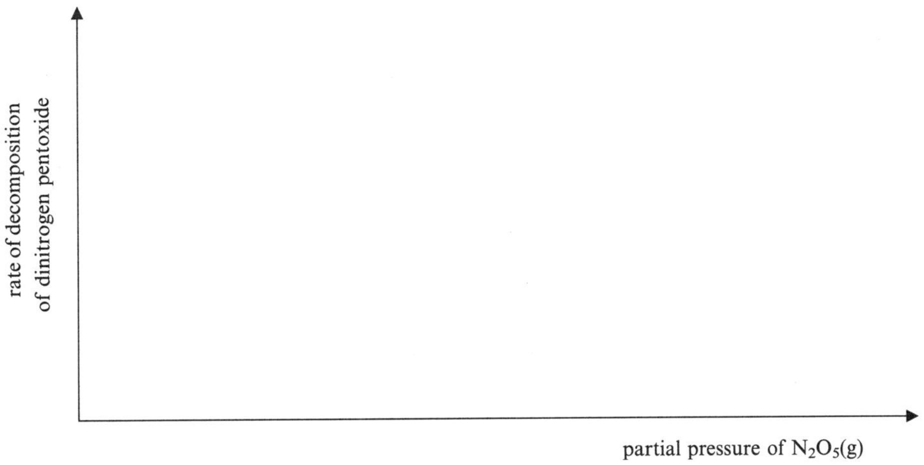

rate of decomposition
of dinitrogen pentoxide

partial pressure of $N_2O_5(g)$

**(1 mark)**

(iii) State how the order of this decomposition reaction could be confirmed from the graph you have drawn in (c)(ii) above.

.......................................................................................................................

.......................................................................................................................

**(1 mark)**

**Total: 11 marks**

**End of Paper 3**

# Longman Examination Board

## General Certificate of Education

## Chemistry

## Paper 4 (Module)

Time: 60 minutes

| Question number | Mark |
|---|---|
| 1. | |
| 2. | |
| 3. | |
| 4. | |
| Total Mark | |

### Instructions

■ Attempt **all** the questions.

■ Write your answers in the spaces provided.

■ Use a blue or black ink pen or ball-point.

### Information for candidates

■ The number of marks for each question or part-question is given in brackets.

■ The total mark for each question is given at the end of each question.

■ The periodic table is printed on page vi and contains all relative atomic masses.

■ **The maximum mark for this paper is 60.**

Margin to be used by examiners to record their marks and the totals

---

1. (a) State **two** general characteristics of ionic compounds.

........................................................................................................................

........................................................................................................................

........................................................................................................................

**(2 marks)**

(b) State what is meant by the term *standard molar lattice enthalpy* of an ionic compound.

........................................................................................................................

........................................................................................................................

**(2 marks)**

(c) State **two** factors which affect the value of the lattice enthalpy of a binary ionic solid.

........................................................................................................................

........................................................................................................................

**(2 marks)**

*Leave margin blank*

(d) Calculate the standard molar lattice enthalpy of silver chloride from the Born–Haber cycle below.

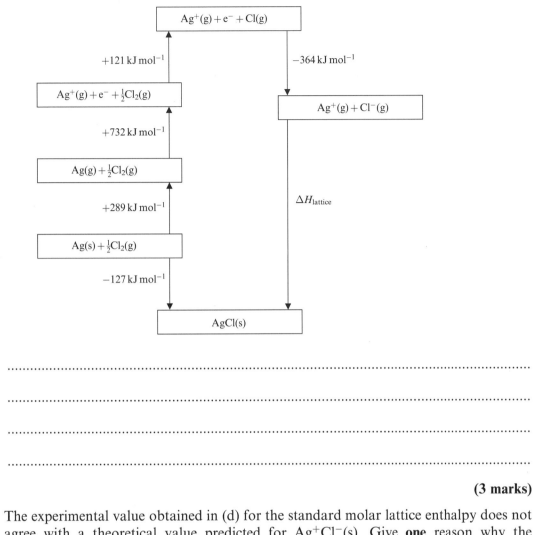

..................................................................................................................................

..................................................................................................................................

..................................................................................................................................

..................................................................................................................................

**(3 marks)**

(e) The experimental value obtained in (d) for the standard molar lattice enthalpy does not agree with a theoretical value predicted for $Ag^+Cl^-(s)$. Give **one** reason why the experimental and theoretical values are different.

..................................................................................................................................

**(1 mark)**

**Total: 10 marks**

2. (a) Complete the following table.

| Ion | Number of bonding pairs of electrons | Number of non-bonding pairs of electrons | Shape of ion |
|---|---|---|---|
| Nitronium, $NO_2^+$ | 4 | 0 | |
| Chlorate(V), $ClO_3^-$ | 3 | | Trigonal pyramidal |
| Hydronium, $H_3O^+$ | | 1 | |
| Ammonium, $NH_4^+$ | | 0 | |

**(3 marks)**

**Turn over**

(b)  Explain **each** of the following.
    (i)  The boiling point of hydrogen fluoride, HF, is the highest of all the hydrogen halides.

........................................................................................................................

........................................................................................................................

........................................................................................................................

**(2 marks)**

    (ii)  In non-aqueous media, ethanoic acid exists as dimeric molecules $(CH_3COOH)_2$.

........................................................................................................................

........................................................................................................................

........................................................................................................................

**(2 marks)**

    (iii)  Water in the solid state is less dense than water in the liquid state.

........................................................................................................................

........................................................................................................................

........................................................................................................................

**(2 marks)**

(c)  (i)  Explain the processes that occur when an ionic solid such as sodium chloride dissolves in water.

........................................................................................................................

........................................................................................................................

........................................................................................................................

**(3 marks)**

    (ii)  Explain why some ionic salts dissolve in water exothermically whereas others dissolve endothermically.

........................................................................................................................

........................................................................................................................

........................................................................................................................

**(2 marks)**

(d)  (i)  State the type of ionic crystal structure and the coordination number of the cation in sodium chloride.

........................................................................................................................

**(2 marks)**

    (ii)  Explain why the answer to (d)(i) would be different for caesium chloride.

........................................................................................................................

**(1 mark)**

**Total: 17 marks**

**3.** (a) Aqueous silver nitrate is added to aqueous sodium halides, NaCl(aq), NaBr(aq) and NaI(aq) in three separate test tubes. One sample from each of the resulting mixtures is exposed to direct sunlight and another sample is treated with excess aqueous ammonia.

(i) Describe the observations for each halide.

**NaCl(aq)**

Addition of $AgNO_3$(aq) ..................................................................

Exposure to sunlight ..................................................................

Treatment with $NH_3$(aq) ..................................................................

**(3 marks)**

**NaBr(aq)**

Addition of $AgNO_3$(aq) ..................................................................

Exposure to sunlight ..................................................................

Treatment with $NH_3$(aq) ..................................................................

**(3 marks)**

**NaI(aq)**

Addition of $AgNO_3$(aq) ..................................................................

Exposure to sunlight ..................................................................

Treatment with $NH_3$(aq) ..................................................................

**(3 marks)**

(ii) How would the observations in (a)(i) above differ on using aqueous sodium fluoride?

..................................................................

**(1 mark)**

(b) When gaseous chlorine is bubbled into cold dilute aqueous sodium hydroxide, a *disproportionation* reaction takes place. Write an equation for the reaction and explain the meaning of the term *disproportionation*.

..................................................................

..................................................................

..................................................................

**(3 marks)**

(c) Explain why cold water does not react with tetrachloromethane, $CCl_4$, but does react violently with silicon tetrachloride, $SiCl_4$, to give off hydrogen chloride.

..................................................................

..................................................................

..................................................................

**(2 marks)**

**Total: 15 marks**

**Turn over**

4. (a) Describe briefly, including all essential detail, the manufacture of sulphuric acid from sulphur. Your answer should include chemical equations and a discussion of why the operating conditions are so chosen.

*Leave margin blank*

..................................................................................................................................

..................................................................................................................................

..................................................................................................................................

..................................................................................................................................

..................................................................................................................................

..................................................................................................................................

..................................................................................................................................

..................................................................................................................................

..................................................................................................................................

**(6 marks)**

(b) The reaction between ethanol and ethanoic acid can be represented by the equation

$$C_2H_5OH + CH_3COOH \rightleftharpoons CH_3COOC_2H_5 + H_2O; \quad \Delta H = -2.0 \, kJ \, mol^{-1}$$

When equal amounts of moles of ethanol and ethanoic acid are mixed with concentrated sulphuric acid, acting as a *homogeneous* catalyst, and allowed to reach equilibrium at 298 K, the resulting mixture contains twice as much ester as ethanoic acid.

(i) Write an expression for the equilibrium constant, $K_c$, for this reaction and determine the value at 298 K.

..................................................................................................................................

..................................................................................................................................

..................................................................................................................................

..................................................................................................................................

..................................................................................................................................

..................................................................................................................................

**(4 marks)**

(ii) If the temperature is increased from 298 K to 343 K state, giving your reasoning, what happens to

**I** – the percentage of ethanol converted to ester

..................................................................................................................................

..................................................................................................................................

**II** – the rate at which equilibrium is established.

..................................................................................................................................

..................................................................................................................................

**(4 marks)**

(c)  (i) Distinguish between *homogeneous* and *heterogeneous* catalysts.

.......................................................................................................................

.......................................................................................................................

**(1 mark)**

(ii)  Draw and label reaction profiles for the catalysed and uncatalysed esterification reaction in (b) above. Draw both profiles on the same axes below.

reaction pathway

**(3 marks)**

**Total: 18 marks**

**End of Paper 4**

## Longman
## Examination Board

## General Certificate of Education

## Chemistry

## Paper 5 (Synoptic)

**Time: 90 minutes**

| Question number | Mark |
|---|---|
| 1. | |
| 2. | |
| 3. | |
| 4. | |
| 5. | |
| Total Mark | |

### Instructions

■ Attempt **all** the questions in **Section A (60 marks)** and **Section B (25 marks)**.

■ Write your answers in blue or black ink pen or ball-point on separate paper.

■ Allow **five** minutes for reading the comprehension passage in **Section B**.

### Information for candidates

■ The number of marks for each question or part-question is given in brackets.

■ The total mark for each question is given at the end of each question.

■ The periodic table is printed on page vi and contains all relative atomic masses.

■ **The maximum mark for this paper is 85.**

---

### Section A

1. (a)  (i)  Draw the full structural formula of benzenecarbaldehyde (benzaldehyde).

**(1 mark)**

   (ii)  Benzenecarbaldehyde is formed when (dichloromethyl)benzene, $C_6H_5CHCl_2$, is hydrolysed by boiling water. Write a balanced equation for this reaction.

**(1 mark)**

   (iii)  In the hydrolysis of the (dichloromethyl)benzene in (a)(ii) above, −OH is thought to replace −Cl to give an unstable dihydroxy compound. On this basis, predict the product formed when (trichloromethyl)benzene is hydrolysed by boiling water.

**(1 mark)**

   (b)  Benzenecarbaldehyde may be used to synthesise a number of compounds, including α-amyl-cinnamaldehyde, with a jasmine perfume and a structure as shown below.

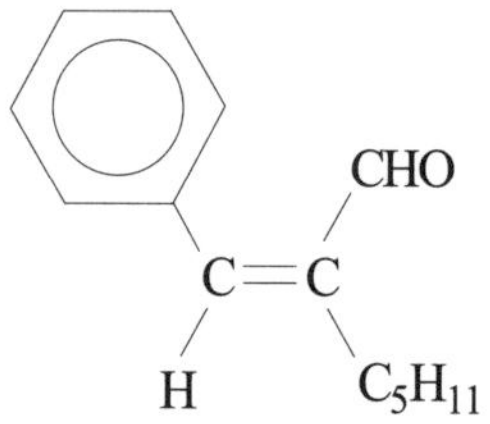

   (i)  State the type of isomerism possible in α-amyl-cinnamaldehyde by virtue of the presence of the carbon–carbon double bond.  **(1 mark)**

(ii) Describe the **observations** you could expect to make if α-amyl-cinnamaldehyde is treated separately under appropriate conditions with

**I** – aqueous ammoniacal silver nitrate solution

**II** – aqueous bromine. **(2 marks)**

(iii) Draw the structure of the compound you would expect to be formed if α-amyl-cinnamaldehyde were treated with hydrogen bromide. **(2 marks)**

(c) (i) Examine the reaction scheme below and then write the names and structural formulae for the aromatic compunds **A** to **E**. **(5 marks)**

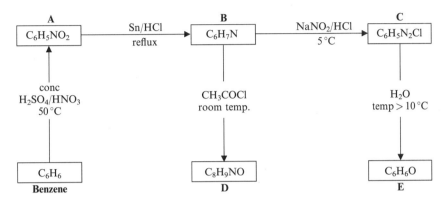

(ii) Give the name and structure of the product formed when **E** is treated with aqueous bromine. **(2 marks)**

**Total: 15 marks**

2. (a) Explain the terms:

(i) Brønsted–Lowry acid and base; **(1 mark)**

(ii) Lewis acid and base. **(1 mark)**

(b) Aluminium chloride, $AlCl_3$, is a Lewis acid and is used as a catalyst in the alkylation of benzene (Friedel–Crafts reaction). Show the mechanism for the reaction between benzene and methyl chloride to form methylbenzene. **(3 marks)**

(c) The pH of a *buffer solution* is given by the relationship $pH = pK_a + \log_{10}([salt]/[acid])$.

(i) State what is meant by the term *buffer solution*. **(1 mark)**

(ii) A certain mass of sodium propanoate, $C_2H_5COONa$, is dissolved in $1000\,cm^3$ of aqueous propanoic acid, of concentration $0.18\,mol\,dm^{-3}$, to give a solution with a pH of 5.2 at 298 K. Calculate the mass of sodium propanoate, assuming no change in volume when the salt was dissolved in the acid.

(The acid dissociation constant for propanoic acid at 298 K is $1.4 \times 10^{-5}\,mol\,dm^{-3}$.) **(3 marks)**

(d) (i) Sketch the variation in pH when aqueous sodium hydroxide of concentration $0.100\,mol\,dm^{-3}$ is added to $25.0\,cm^3$ of aqueous propanoic acid of concentration $0.100\,mol\,dm^{-3}$. **(2 marks)**

(ii) State the significance of the pH value when $12.5\,cm^3$ of the aqueous sodium hydroxide has been added in (d)(i) and state the pH value. **(2 marks)**

(iii) State the name of the indicator you would choose for the titration of aqueous propanoic acid with aqueous sodium hydroxide and give the reason for your choice. **(2 marks)**

**Total: 15 marks**

**Turn over**

3. (a) Aluminium is extracted from bauxite. The ore is a hydrated form of aluminium oxide containing substantial quantities of iron(III) oxide and titanium(IV) oxide. The bauxite is crushed and purified by a process that involves heating under pressure with aqueous sodium hydroxide and removing the impurities, followed by the formation of aluminium hydroxide and its thermal decomposition into aluminium oxide. The purified oxide is dissolved in molten cryolite – sodium hexafluoroaluminate(III) – and the aluminium extracted by electrolysis.

   (i) State what happens when the bauxite is heated under pressure with sodium hydroxide and explain how this process can lead to the removal of some impurities.

         **(2 marks)**

   (ii) Write a balanced equation for the thermal decomposition of aluminium hydroxide.

         **(1 mark)**

   (iii) Write the ionic formula for sodium hexafluoroaluminate(III) and state the shape of the hexafluoroaluminate(III) ion.   **(2 marks)**

   (iv) Calculate the quantity of electricity, in coulombs, required to produce 27.0 tonnes (27 000 kg) of aluminium in the electrolytic cell. (The charge on the electron is $1.60 \times 10^{-19}$ C and the Avogadro Constant, $L$, is $6.02 \times 10^{23}$ mol$^{-1}$.)   **(2 marks)**

   (v) State the economic consequence of your answer in (iv).   **(1 mark)**

   (vi) State a property of aluminium metal that makes it suitable for large-scale industrial use and give an example of the industrial use based on the property.

         **(1 mark)**

(b) Titanium occurs chiefly as its oxide $TiO_2$. In the extraction of the metal, the titanium(IV) oxide ore is heated with carbon and chlorine to form the molecular chloride $TiCl_4$. This titanium(IV) chloride is finally reduced by heating with molten sodium in sealed vessels.

   (i) Write a balanced equation for the reaction between titanium(IV) oxide, carbon and chlorine.   **(1 mark)**

   (ii) Suggest why titanium is a rather expensive metal to manufacture.   **(1 mark)**

(c) Titanium(IV) chloride, $TiCl_4$, and aluminium triethyl, $Al(C_2H_5)_3$, are used in the manufacture of high-density poly(ethene).

   (i) What is the function of $TiCl_4$ and $Al(C_2H_5)_3$, in the manufacture of poly(ethene)?

         **(1 mark)**

   (ii) Suggest why the liquid titanium(IV) chloride must be kept in dry storage tanks.

         **(1 mark)**

   (iii) Explain why aluminium triethyl may be classed as a Lewis acid.   **(2 marks)**

         **Total: 15 marks**

4. (a) Give the name of one example of each of the following types of polymer and the draw the full structural formula of the **linkage** between the repeating units in the polymer.

   (i) polyester   **(2 marks)**

   (ii) protein.   **(2 marks)**

(b) Di(benzoyl)peroxide, $C_6H_5.CO.O.O.CO.C_6H_5$, undergoes symmetrical *homolytic fission* when it is used as an initiator in *free radical* polymerisation processes.

   (i) Explain the meaning of the term *homolytic fission*.   **(2 marks)**

   (ii) State the essential feature of a *free radical*.   **(1 mark)**

   (iii) Write an equation to show the symmetrical homolytic fission of di(benzoyl)-peroxide.   **(1 mark)**

(c) The Nylons are classed as polyamides. Nylon-6,6 is one of the first to be made and is derived from 1,6-diaminohexane and hexane-1,6-dioic acid.

(i) Draw the structure of Nylon-6,6. **(1 mark)**

(ii) State **one** physical property of nylon and relate the property to the structure of the polymer. **(1 mark)**

(iii) Another different Nylon may be derived from 1,4-diaminobenzene and benzene-1,4-dicarboxylic acid whose formulae are shown below.

Draw the structure of the repeating unit of this polymer and suggest one physical property of this Nylon that will be completely different from the physical properties of Nylon-6,6, giving a reason for your answer. **(3 marks)**

(d) Synthetic organic polymeric materials are part of everyday life. Give **two** disadvantages of these materials, stating clearly the reasons for your answers. **(2 marks)**

**Total: 15 marks**

**End of Section A**

## Section B

5. Read the following passage carefully then answer the following questions (a) to (j).

### A Complex Environment?

In 1962 Rachel Carson published *Silent Spring*, a book linking the reduction in bird life in the UK with the use of the insecticide DDT (dichlorodiphenyltrichloroethane). In 1997 The Royal Society for the Protection of Birds (RSPB) published a report linking the decline in the numbers of 12 important species of British birds with the increasing use of agrochemicals.

In 1998 The Royal Society of Chemistry published an article by Professor David R Williams concerning the accumulation in the environment of metal complexing agents such as EDTA (ethylenediaminetetraacetic acid) which is used in agrochemicals. The article described DDT as a direct the threat to birds but agrochemicals as an indirect threat because birds starve from the scarcity of insects on treated crops.

Complexing agents have a wide range of uses with a total of more than 70% being used in agrochemicals, detergents, water treatment and the printing, paper, pulp and textile industry. Citric acid (2-hydroxy-1,2,3-propanetricarboxylic acid) was one of the traditional complexing agents used by the printing and textile industries to prevent calcium in hard water from forming stains. EDTA and NTA (nitrilotriacetate) replaced it about fifty years ago and about 10 000 tonnes of these two agents are now used annually in the UK alone. EDTA was patented in Germany in 1935 and in the US in 1946. It is marketed under various trade names and more than 30% of world production is used in detergents. However, some parts of the US now ban its use whilst some countries restrict its use and specify a maximum allowable level in river water. EDTA can be incinerated and can also be photodegraded by intense sunlight but it is not readily biodegradable and its complexes may persist in the environment for up to fifteen years.

EDTA has been used in medical treatments to remove metals such as lead but patients frequently experience side effects due to the removal of essential metals such as magnesium because the complexing agent is non-specific. Experiments with living rat kidney cells in growth media containing less than $1 \times 10^{-4}$ mol dm$^{-3}$ Na$_2$H$_2$EDTA(aq) have found that many cells die or lose

**Turn over**

their reproductive ability. These results were obtained even though there was insufficient sodium salt to combine with all the calcium ions present in the growth media. However, a survey carried out in 1992 showed that concentrations of EDTA in river water and sewage effluent were less than $1 \times 10^{-6}$ mol dm$^{-3}$. In 1993 the average concentration of EDTA in drinking water was found to be $4.4 \times 10^{-8}$ mol dm$^{-3}$ which is approximately 17% of the maximum level recommended in 1973 by the WHO (World Health Organization). Some other experiments have suggested that a concentration as high as $1 \times 10^{-3}$ mol dm$^{-3}$ $Na_2H_2EDTA(aq)$ would show no effect on living human cells.

The molecular structure of EDTA and of NTA contains carboxylic acid groups (see Fig. 1).

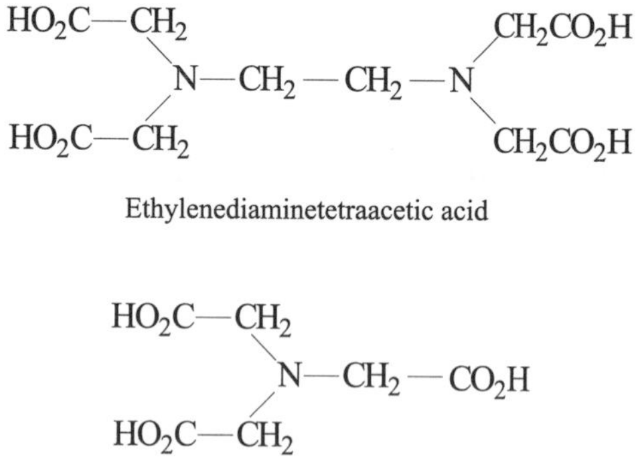

Ethylenediaminetetraacetic acid

nitrilotriacetic acid

Figure 1

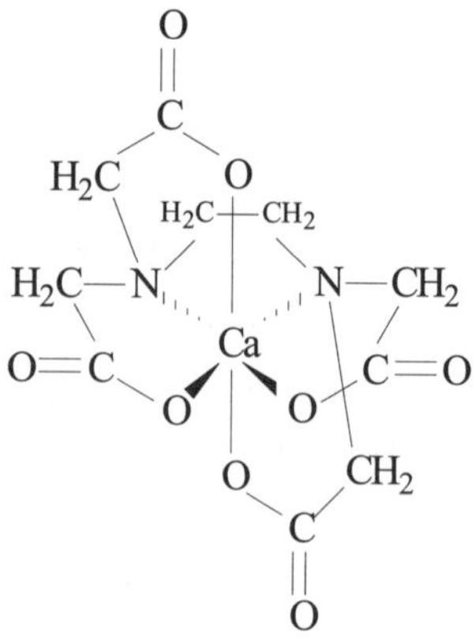

Figure 2

The $EDTA^{4-}$ anion is a hexadentate ligand that establishes bonds with metal cations to form octahedral complexes (see Fig. 2). Research chemists, with the help of computer simulation, are attempting to design and synthesise biodegradable ligands that are more specific and efficient for industrial use. For example, EDDS (ethylenediaminedisuccinic acid) has a similar structure to that of EDTA but is a more efficient and biodegradable complexing agent for most applications (see Fig. 3). EDDS can form complex ions with copper and nickel but its ability depends upon the pH. In a neutral solution, the ligand combines at least four times more readily with nickel ions than with copper ions whereas in an alkaline solution, it combines equally well with either metal ion.

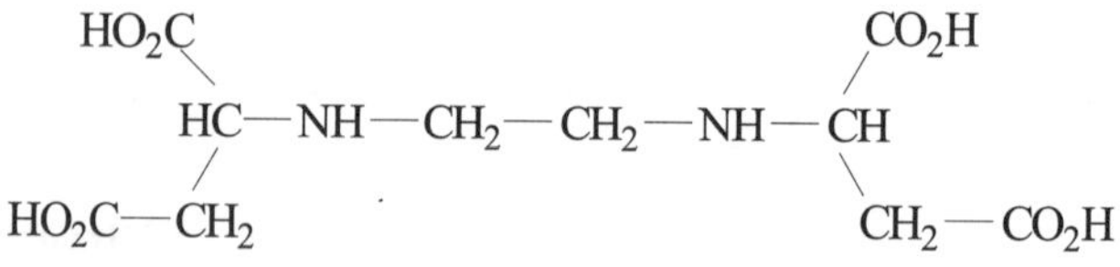

ethylenediaminedisuccinic acid

Figure 3

---

(a) For large-scale commercial and industrial use, suggest one advantage of citric acid over EDTA and one advantage of EDTA over citric acid. **(2 marks)**

(b) Write the structural formula of citric acid, identify those atoms that could be used when citric acid acts as a ligand and suggest an explanation for citric acid being classified as a bidentate ligand. **(3 marks)**

(c) State the number of bonds formed by one EDTA ligand with one metal ion and suggest, giving your reasons, how many bonds one NTA ligand might form with one metal ion. **(3 marks)**

(d) Give the name of the type of bonding between EDTA and Ca as shown in Fig. 2 and explain, in terms of electrons, how one of these bonds might have formed. **(3 marks)**

(e) Suggest **two** products most likely to be formed when EDTA is incinerated and explain their effect, if any, upon the environment. **(3 marks)**

(f) What would be the charge, if any, on the species represented by Fig. 2?     **(1 mark)**

(g) Calculate the maximum mass in grams of calcium that could be removed from hard water by treatment with $100\,cm^3$ of a solution of $EDTA^{4-}(aq)$ of concentration $1.00 \times 10^{-4}\,mol\,dm^{-3}$.     **(3 marks)**

(h) By comparing the structures of EDTA, NTA and EDDS shown in Figs 1 and 3, write down the structural formula of succinic acid and gives its systematic name.     **(2 marks)**

(i) Why might EDTA, NTA and EDDS be more efficient ligands in solutions of pH greater than 7?

     **(2 marks)**

(j) Given that 1,1,1-trichloro-2,2-di(4-chlorophenyl)ethane is the systematic name for dichlorodiphenyltrichloroethane, write the structural formula of the molecule and deduce whether or not the insecticide would be soluble in water.     **(3 marks)**

**Total: 25 marks**

**End of Paper 5**

# Solutions to practice exam papers

## Paper 1 (Module) marking scheme

**1.** (a)    (i)    Mass number ($A$) is the <u>number of protons and neutrons</u> in the nucleus of an atom. ✓

            Relative atomic mass ($A_r$) is the <u>ratio of the average mass per atom</u> of the natural isotopic composition of an element <u>to one-twelfth of the mass of an atom of the nuclide $^{12}$C</u>. ✓        **2 marks**

      (ii)    11 protons (atomic no.11), 11 neutrons (mass no. 22–11) and 10 electrons (Na$^+$) ✓        **1 mark**

   (b)    (i)    $A_r(Br) = 80$ (=50% of 79 + 50% of 81)          ✓        **1 mark**

      (ii)    Peak heights in ratio $1:2:1$ ✓ at mass/charge ratios of 158, 160 and 162. ✓        **2 marks**

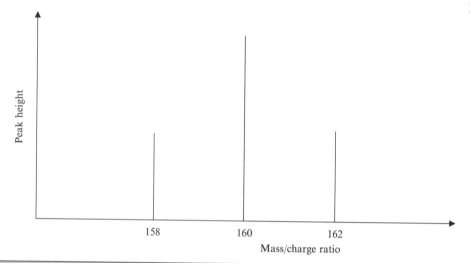

**TIP**

Remember that there is twice the possibility of a molecule having mass 160 than 158 or 162. The probabilities are 158: $\frac{1}{2} \times \frac{1}{2}$; 160: $2 \times \frac{1}{2} \times \frac{1}{2}$; 162: $\frac{1}{2} \times \frac{1}{2}$, i.e. 0.25 : 0.5 : 0.25. Check $0.25 + 0.5 + 0.25 = 1.0$ because the total probability must be 1.0. Make sure you also know the mass spectrum for chlorine – another favourite.

   (c)    (i)

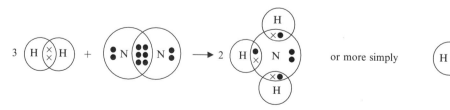

                                                      ✓

                                                   ✓ **1 mark**

**TIP**

Soldium chloride is ionic so show that electrons are transferred to form separate ions. Ammonia is covalent so show that pairs of electrons are shared to form bonds. Make sure you show non-bonding electron pairs – you might lose these easy marks if you leave them out.

      (ii)

                                                         ✓

                                                         **1 mark**

(iii) **sodium chloride**: <u>ionic bonding</u> ✓ <u>high melting point</u> crystal owing to <u>strong electrostatic forces of attraction</u> between <u>oppositely charged</u> $Na^+$ and $Cl^-$ ions. ✓

**ammonia**: <u>covalent bonding</u> ✓ <u>low boiling point</u> gas and <u>non-conductor</u> in the liquid state owing to only <u>weak forces of attraction between the molecules</u> ✓ whose atoms are held together within the molecule by strong covalent bonds. **4 marks**

**Total: 12 marks**

**2.** (a) Melting: as the temperature rises, the particles <u>vibrate with increasing energy</u> ✓ until they <u>break free from their fixed positions</u> ✓ and the solid melts.

Boiling: as the temperature continues to rise, the <u>number of particles escaping from the liquid increases</u> ✓ as their energy rises until the <u>vapour pressure reaches atmospheric pressure</u> ✓ and the liquid boils. **maximum 3 marks**

> **TIP**
>
> Examiners will expect you to be able to describe and interpret melting, evaporating, boiling, subliming and dissolving qualitatively in terms of an elementary kinetic model of the motion and energy of particles. Simple answers are wanted here but you might get a bonus mark for mentioning that particles vibrate in a solid but also translate and rotate in a liquid or gas.

(b) (i) The <u>standard molar enthalpy change</u> of a process is <u>independent of the means or route</u> by which the process takes place. ✓ **1 mark**

(ii)

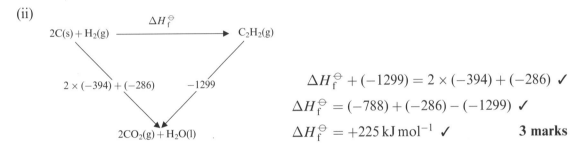

$$\Delta H_f^{\ominus} + (-1299) = 2 \times (-394) + (-286)\ ✓$$
$$\Delta H_f^{\ominus} = (-788) + (-286) - (-1299)\ ✓$$
$$\Delta H_f^{\ominus} = +225\,\text{kJ}\,\text{mol}^{-1}\ ✓ \qquad \textbf{3 marks}$$

> **TIP**
>
> Draw a cycle when you tackle Hess's law calculations and you will usually gain more marks than candidates who just produce a jumble of figures. Remember to take account of the amounts (moles) of each substance in your cycle and to give the units $(\text{kJ}\,\text{mol}^{-1})$ of the enthalpy change in your answer. Omitting the units is a very common mistake.

(c) (i) Energy released when bonds form is $2 \times 2 \times E(C=O) + 3 \times 2 \times E(OH)$

$= 2 \times 2 \times 805 + 3 \times 2 \times 6464$ ✓

Energy absorbed when bonds break is

$E(C-C) + 5 \times E(C-H) \times E(C-O) + E(O-H) + 3 \times E(O=O)$

$= 347 + 5 \times 413 + 358 + 464 + 3 \times 498$ ✓

Predicted enthalpy change of combustion is

$[347 + 5 \times 413 + 358 + 464 + 3 \times 498] - [2 \times 2 \times 805 + 3 \times 2 \times 464]$

$= 4728 - 6004 = 1276\,\text{kJ}\,\text{mol}^{-1}$ ✓ **3 marks**

(ii) The bond energies are only <u>average values</u> ✓ so, for example, the energies needed to break the two O−H bonds in the water molecule may be different from each other and different from the energy required to break the O−H bond in the alcohol molecule. **1 mark**

> **TIP**
>
> Bond formation is always exothermic ($\Delta H$ is negative).
> Bond breaking is always endothermic ($\Delta H$ is positive).

(d)  <u>Lattice energy</u> ✓ of the ionic crystal and the <u>hydration energies of its constituent ions.</u> ✓

**2 marks**

**Total: 13 marks**

**3.** (a)  (i)  Correct <u>position of the values</u> for the single <u>outer electron and the innermost pair</u> ✓ <u>and the increasing values for the inner eight</u> electrons ✓  **2 marks**

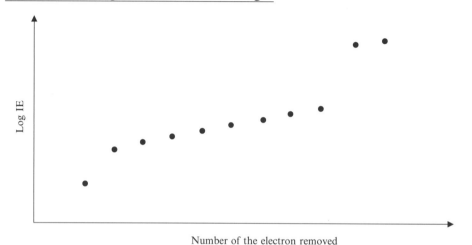

Number of the electron removed

> **TIP**
>
> The one outer-shell electron is easiest to remove because the inner shells screen it from the charge on the nucleus. The two innermost-shell electrons will be hardest to remove. Note the upward slope in the graph corresponding to the increasing difficulty of removing the eight inner-shell electrons from an increasingly positive ion. Why do we plot logarithms?

(ii)  General fall of peaks and troughs ✓ fall from at.no. 4 to 5 or from 12 to 13 ✓ and fall from at.no. 7 to 8 or from 15 to 16 ✓  **3 marks**

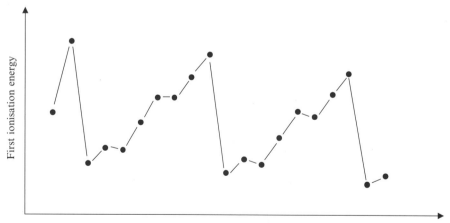

Atomic number

> **TIP**
>
> Each of the three p-orbitals takes one electron until the fourth is added to make a pair. This explains the small drop between at.nos. 7 and 8 and 15 and 16. Note that the first ionisation energy within any Group of the periodic table (e.g. Noble Gases: at.nos. 2, 10 and 18) decreases with increasing atomic number. Be prepared to explain the shape of this graph.

(b) (i) Sodium **Observations**: the <u>silvery</u> metal melts, becomes <u>spherical in shape</u> and with a <u>hissing sound</u> it <u>runs randomly across the surface</u> of the water. ✓ (any two underlined to gain the mark)

**Equation**: $Na(s) + H_2O(l) \rightarrow NaOH(aq) + \frac{1}{2}H_2(g)$ ✓     **2 marks**

> **TIP**
>
> Don't confuse observations with interpretations. Many candidates lose marks by stating what they think is happening (e.g. sodium and water react to give off hydrogen) instead of describing what they see.
> Remember: **OBSERVATIONS** means **WHAT YOU SEE, HEAR AND SMELL!**

(ii) Chlorine **Observations**: cold water turns a very <u>pale green</u> colour when <u>greenish-yellow gas</u> is bubbled into it. ✓

**Equation**: $Cl_2(g) + H_2O(l) \rightarrow HCl(aq) + HClO(aq)$ ✓     **2 marks**

(c) (i) An amphoteric oxide: $Al_2O_3$ ✓     **1 mark**

(ii) A giant covalent oxide: $SiO_2$ ✓     **1 mark**

> **TIP**
>
> Examiners will test your grasp of classifying oxides as basic ($CaO$), acidic ($SO_3$), amphoteric ($Al_2O_3$), neutral ($CO$), giant covalent ($SiO_2$), giant ionic ($Na_2O$), etc. and the pattern of the classification in relation to the periodic table. You should also be aware of the so-called mixed acidic oxides of, for example, nitrogen: $N_2O_4 + H_2O \rightarrow HNO_2 + HNO_3$.

(d) **Example 1**: Except for <u>lithium</u> which <u>forms the nitride</u>, $Li_3N$, ✓ the <u>alkali metals</u> do <u>not</u> <u>react directly with nitrogen</u>. ✓ When heated in air <u>lithium forms the oxide</u>, $Li_2O$, ✓ but the other <u>alkali metals form peroxides</u>, $Na_2O_2$, and <u>superoxides</u>, $KO_2$. ✓ <u>Lithium carbonate or nitrate decomposes completely into lithium oxide</u> in a bunsen flame ✓ but the <u>other alkali metal carbonate and nitrates do not</u>. ✓

**Example 2**: Except for <u>fluorine</u> in which <u>water burns</u> ✓ to form hydrogen fluoride and oxygen, the <u>halogens dissolve and disproportionate</u> ✓ in water. <u>Silver fluoride is soluble</u> in water ✓ but the other <u>silver halides</u> are only <u>sparingly soluble</u>. ✓

**maximum 4 marks**

**Total: 15 marks**

> **TIP**
>
> Remember that the elements and their compounds in the period from lithium to fluorine inclusive have some properties that are not typical of their Group.
> Learn one example of a typical behaviour for **each** Group in **your syllabus**.
> The contrast between $CCl_4$ and $SiCl_4$ is popular with examiners.

**4.** (a) (i) The <u>uneven splitting</u> of a <u>single bond</u> ✓ between two atoms sharing a pair of electrons so that <u>one of the atoms retains both electrons</u>. ✓     **2 marks**

(ii) A <u>molecule</u> or an <u>anion</u> ✓ able to act as an <u>electron-pair donor</u> or a <u>Lewis base</u>. ✓     **2 marks**

> **TIP**
>
> *Homo* = same (think of *homo*geneous catalyst, *homo*logous series).
> *Hetero* = different (think of *hetero*sexual).
> An anglo*phile* loves the English, a franco*phile* loves the French and a nucleo*phile* loves the nucleus or region of POSITIVE charge.

(b)  (i)  Electrophilic addition ✓  **1 mark**

(ii)

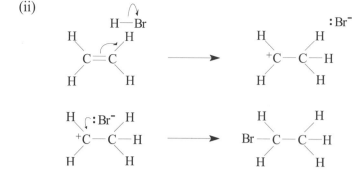

for correct <u>shifts of electron pairs</u> ✓ showing formation of <u>carbocation</u> ✓

for correctly showing the <u>nucleophilic attack of the bromide ion</u> ✓  **3 marks**

> **TIP**
>
> You must use a curly arrow **very accurately** to show the direction of movement of **a pair of electrons**. The tail of a curly arrow starts precisely either at a lone pair or at the centre of a bond(ed pair). The head of the curly arrow must show precisely where the electron-pair is going. Do **not** use curly arrows to show the movement of atoms, ions or molecules.

(iii)  The <u>colourless</u> ethene <u>gas</u> would turn the <u>red–brown</u> aqueous bromine pale orange and finally <u>colourless</u>. ✓ (initial and final colours to gain the mark)  **1 mark**

(iv)  2-bromoethanol ✓ and 1-bromo-2-chloroethane. ✓ A nucleophilic ethene molecule reacts with a bromine molecule to form the electrophilic <u>carbocation</u> $^+CH_2CH_2Br$ which can be <u>attacked by nucleophilic water molecules</u> $H_2O$: and anions such as $:OH^-$ and $:Cl^-$ as well as $:Br^-$. ✓  **3 marks**

> **TIP**
>
> Examiners expect you to apply your knowledge to unfamiliar situations. You should know that carbocations are positive ions that will be attacked by any available nucleophiles. You should also know that nucleophiles are anions or molecules with at least one lone pair of electrons that can be donated to form a covalent bond.

(c)  (i)  aqueous sodium hydroxide ✓ with the mixture boiled under reflux. ✓  **2 marks**

(ii)  ethanolic potassium cyanide ✓ with the mixture boiled under reflux. ✓  **2 marks**

(iii)  nucleophilic substitution. ✓  **1 mark**

> **TIP**
>
> Look for the polarity in the halogenoalkane molecule (Br is more electronegative than C) and decide where to point the curly arrow head. Look for the lone electron-pair on the nucleophile and decide where to put the curly arrow tail.
>
> Remember to put the charge on the transition state ion. Examiners will look for it.

(iv)

<u>nucleophilic attack</u> ✓ correctly shown leading to <u>transition state anion</u> ✓ <u>elimination of bromide ion</u> ✓ leading to the alsohol.  **3 marks**

Stereochemistry important but not required in this answer. Possible bonus mark?

**Total: 20 marks**

# Paper 2 (Module) marking scheme

**1.** (a)    A state in which the intensive <u>physical and chemical properties</u> of a system (e.g. <u>pressure</u> and <u>concentration</u>) are <u>constant</u> because opposing <u>kinetic molecular processes</u> are taking place at exactly the <u>same balancing rates</u>. ✓  **1 mark**

(b)    (i)    $K_p = \dfrac{p_{C_2H_5OH}}{p_{C_2H_2} \times p_{H_2O}}$  **1 mark**

> **TIP**
>
> Many candidates get this wrong. By convention, the rule is:
> partial pressures of products to appropriate power in the numerator
> and partial pressures of reactants to appropriate power in the denominator.
> So remember: **products on top** and **reactants underneath**.

(ii)    **Temperature**: The amount of ethanol in the equilibrium mixture would <u>decrease</u> ✓ because according to <u>Le Chatelier's Principle</u>, an <u>increase in temperature</u> will <u>favour</u> the <u>endothermic direction</u> of a reversible reaction. ✓  **2 marks**

**Total pressure**: The amount of ethanol in the equilibrium mixture would <u>increase</u> ✓ because according to Le Chatelier's Principle, an increase in total pressure will <u>favour</u> the direction of a reversible reaction corresponding to a <u>decrease in the number of moles of gas</u>. ✓  **2 marks**

> **TIP**
>
> Think of the endothermic reaction absorbing the heat being added to raise the temperature and check the sign of $\Delta H$. Think of the reaction producing fewer gas molecules to take up less room as the pressure is increased and check the number of moles of gas on each side of the equation. These should be easy marks for you.

(iii)    The ethene may polymerise to poly(ethene). ✓  **1 mark**

(iv)    $K_p = 3$ atm/(31 atm × 31 atm) = <u>$3.1 \times 10^{-3}$ atm$^{-1}$</u> ✓ ✓  **2 marks**

(v)    The ethanol must be continuously <u>separated from the equilibrium mixture</u> ✓ and the <u>unreacted ethene</u> must be <u>recycled</u>. ✓  **2 marks**

(c)    (i)    A weak acid is a proton donor that only partially ionises in water. ✓  **1 mark**

(ii)    For a weak acid, HA, the dissociation constant $K_a = [H^+] \times [A^-]/[HA]$ but $[H^+] \approx [A^-]$ so $K_a = [H^+]^2/[HA]$ ✓ but $pK_a = -\log_{10}(K_a/\text{mol dm}^{-3})$ and $pH = -\log_{10}([H^+]/\text{mol dm}^{-3})$, so taking the negative logarithm to the base 10 gives

$pK_a = 2 \times pH + \log_{10}([HA]/\text{mol dm}^{-3})$

Hence pH = {4.74 −(−1.26)}/2 = 3.0 ✓    (Any valid method giving this answer scores 2 marks)  **2 marks**

> **TIP**
>
> Make sure you can handle logs on your calculator (don't confuse $\log_{10}$ with $\ln_e$) and remember these: $pH = -\log_{10}([H^+]/\text{mol dm}^{-3})$, $pOH = -\log_{10}([OH^-]/\text{mol dm}^{-3})$
> $K_w = [H^+][OH^-] = 1 \times 10^{-14}$ mol$^2$ dm$^{-6}$, $pK_w = -\log_{10}(K_w/\text{mol}^2 \text{dm}^{-6})$,
> $pK_w = pH + pOH = 14$, $K_a = [H^+] \times [A^-]/[HA]$ and $pK_a = -\log_{10}(K_a/\text{mol dm}^{-3})$.

(iii)    The <u>ethanoic acid</u> would <u>react with</u> small amounts of <u>alkali</u> ✓ added to the solution and its conjugate base, the <u>ethanoate anions</u>, would <u>react with</u> small amounts of <u>acid</u> ✓ added to the solution so the <u>pH</u> of the solution would <u>not change</u> ✓ significantly.  **3 marks**

**Total: 17 marks**

**2.** (a) (i) A mixture of <u>conc. nitric acid and conc. sulphuric acid</u> ✓ cooled to keep the temperature of the reaction <u>below 55°C</u>. ✓ **2 marks**

**TIP**

The reaction mixture must produce an electrophile.
Make sure you can write the equation for the reaction of concentrated sulphuric acid with concentrated nitric acid: $2H_2SO_4 + HNO_3 \rightarrow 2HSO_4^- + H_3O^+ + NO_2^+$

(ii) Electrophilic substitution. ✓ **1 mark**

(iii)

<u>electrophile/movement of electron pair</u> ✓ formation of <u>Wheland intermediate</u> ✓ <u>formation of the product</u> ✓ **3 marks**

(b) (i) $C_6H_5NH_2$ ✓ **1 mark**

(ii) A mixture of aqueous <u>sodium nitrite and hydrochloric acid</u> ✓ cooled to keep the reaction <u>temperature between 0 and 5°C</u>. ✓ **2 marks**

(iii)

✓ ✓ **2 marks**

**Total: 11 marks**

**3.** (a) (i) The elements and their compounds are good <u>catalysts</u>. ✓ They form a variety of <u>coloured compounds</u> ✓ and <u>complexes</u> ✓ in a <u>variety of oxidation states</u>. ✓ **maximum 2 marks**

**TIP**

The d-shell electrons are responsible for the characteristics of transition metals including properties such as paramagnetism, good electrical conductivity and the ability to act as heterogeneous catalysts. Transition metals form at least one ion with a partially filled d-shell and their aqueous ions are usually coloured. Why are $Sc^{3+}$(aq) and $Zn^{2+}$(aq) colourless?

(ii) **$Mn^{2+}$** $1s^2 2s^2 2p^6 3s^2 3p^6 3d^5$ ✓  **Cr** $1s^2 2s^2 2p^6 3s^3 3p^6 3d^5 4s^1$ ✓ **2 marks**

(iii) These d-block elements <u>do not form an ion with a partially filled d-shell</u>. ✓ **1 mark**

(b) (i) ox. no. V is $+5$ ✓ [reasoning: ox. no. of vanadium $+3 \times (-2) = -1$] **1 mark**

(ii) ox. no. Mn is $+6$ ✓ [reasoning: ox. no. of manganese $+4 \times (-2) = -2$] **1 mark**

(iii) $CrO_4^{2-}$ ✓ **1 mark**

(iv) The solution turns from <u>yellow to orange</u> because the aqueous <u>chromate(VI) reacts with hydrogen ions to form dichromate(VI)</u> ✓:
$2CrO_4^{2-}(aq) + 2H^+(aq) \rightarrow Cr_2O_7^{2-}(aq) + H_2O(l)$ ✓ **2 marks**

(c) (i) octahedral ✓ **1 mark**

(ii) potassium manganate(VII) or dichromate(VI) ✓ or any valid answer
$MnO_4^-(aq) + 8H^+(aq) + 5Fe^{2+}(aq) \rightarrow Mn^{2+}(aq) + 4H_2O(l) + 5Fe^{3+}(aq)$ ✓ or
$Cr_2O_7^{2-}(aq) + 14H^+(aq) + 6Fe^{2+}(aq) \rightarrow 2Cr^{3+}(aq) + 7H_2O(l) + 6Fe^{3+}(aq)$ ✓ **2 marks**

**Total: 13 marks**

**TIP**

Examiners often ask you to write IONIC equations for reactions. Keep them as simple as possible and leave out the spectator ions. For example, the ionic equation for the reaction of aqueous iron(III) chloride with aqueous potassium iodide would be:

$Fe^{3+}(aq) + I^-(aq) \rightarrow Fe^{2+}(aq) + \frac{1}{2}I_2(aq)$.   What spectator ions have been left out?

**4.** (a)   (i)   46 ✓                                                                    **1 mark**

   (ii)   $C_2H_5^+$ ✓                                                            **1 mark**

   (iii)   $C_2H_5O^+$ ✓                                                         **1 mark**

(b)   $-OH$ hydroxyl group ✓                                              **1 mark**

(c)   Compound **X** could be ethanol: $CH_3CH_2OH$ ✓

The three distinct absorptions in the NMR spectrum could correspond to the three H-atoms in the methyl group ($CH_3$), ✓ the two H-atoms in the methylene group ($CH_2$) ✓ and the one H-atom in the hydroxyl group (OH). ✓                **4 marks**

**TIP**

In these types of organic puzzles you should consider all the data provided in the question before jumping to any final conclusion and starting to write down your answers. The last piece of evidence may often be a vital clue to the complete answer. Remember that you can still get good marks for sound reasoning even if your answer isn't complete.

(d)   chromatography ✓ fractional distillation ✓          **2 marks**   **Total: 10 marks**

**5.** (a)   (i)   diamond ✓ graphite ✓                                       **2 marks**

   (ii)   Diamond is a hard non-conductor ✓ because the atoms are held rigidly in fixed positions by four covalent bonds with no electrons free to move. ✓ Graphite is a soft conductor because flat sheets of atoms can slide over each other and in the sheets are mobile delocalised electrons. ✓                                              **3 marks**

(b)   (i)   Caesium acts as a reducing agent by loss of electrons so that its oxidation number increases from 0 to $+1$ as its atoms become positive ions: $3Cs \rightarrow 3Cs^+ + 3e^-$. ✓

Therefore fullerene acts as an oxidising agent by gaining electrons:

$C_{60} + 3e^- \rightarrow C_{60}^{3-}$. ✓                                         **2 marks**

**TIP**

In A-level exams you can assume that the Group 1 alkali metals always form ionic compounds in which the element is a singly charged cation. This is nearly always true but there is evidence for gaseous sodium molecules, $Na_2$.
Is the oxidation number of fluorine always $-1$ in the halogen's compounds?

   (ii)   Mass/g of carbon in one mole of crystals $= 720 + n \times 72.0$

Hence % by mass of carbon is $100 \times (720 + n \times 72.0)/1032 = 97.65$ ✓

$720 + n \times 72.0 = 1032 \times 97.65/100$

$n \times 72.0 = 10.32 \times 97.65 - 720$

$n = (10.32 \times 97.65 - 720)/72.0$

$n = 287.7/72.0$

$n = 4$ ✓                                                          **2 marks**   **Total: 9 marks**

**TIP**

Watch out for the significant figures in 5(b)(ii). Make sure you understand why our mark scheme has occasionally 4 significant figures but mostly 3 and never more than 4 significant figures. Remember always to show all your working. Some candidates don't realise that percentage is $100 \times$ (the part ÷ the whole) or $100 \times$ the fraction.

# Paper 3 (Module) marking scheme

**1.** (a) (i) Optical isomerism ✓ because the molecule has a <u>chiral centre</u> – a <u>carbon atom with four different groups attached</u>: $(CH_3)_2CHCH_2–C_6H_4–$, $CH_3–$, $–COOH$ and $–H$. ✓ **2 marks**

> **TIP**
>
> In isomerism questions look for **four different atoms or groups** bonded to a tetrahedral carbon atom that acts as a chiral centre to give optical isomerism. Remember to look for a carbon–carbon double bond that restricts rotation to give **geometrical isomerism**. Candidates often lose marks by missing optical and geometrical isomers.

(ii) ✓

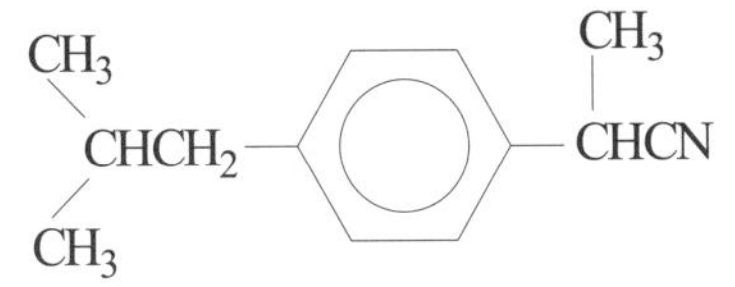

**1 mark**

(b) (i) four ✓ **1 mark**

(ii)

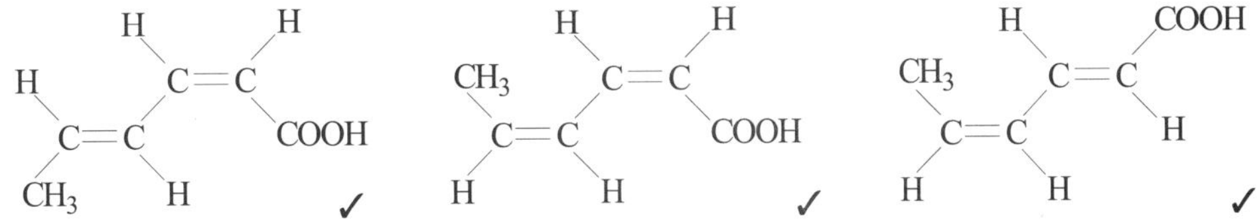

any two structures **maximum 2 marks**

(iii) hexanoic acid ✓ **1 mark**

(c) (i) **2 marks**

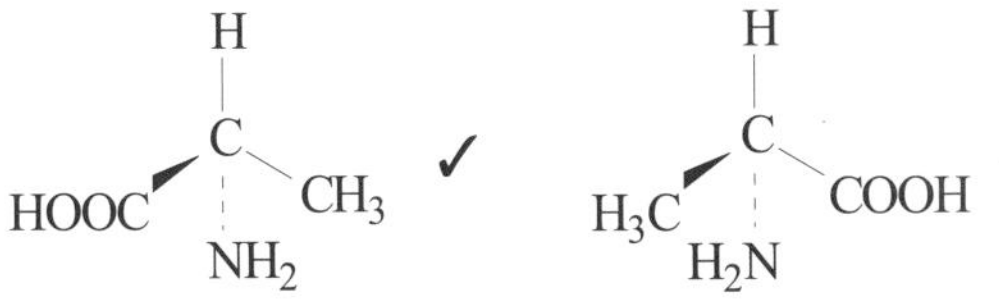

> **TIP**
>
> Examiners will expect you to produce clear **three-dimensional** drawings of optical isomers. Practise drawing diagrams to look like our answer for 1(c)(i).
> You will lose marks if your diagram looks 'flat' and the four bonds seem to be at right angles to each other. It helps to use three different types of line to draw the bonds.

(ii) **2 marks**

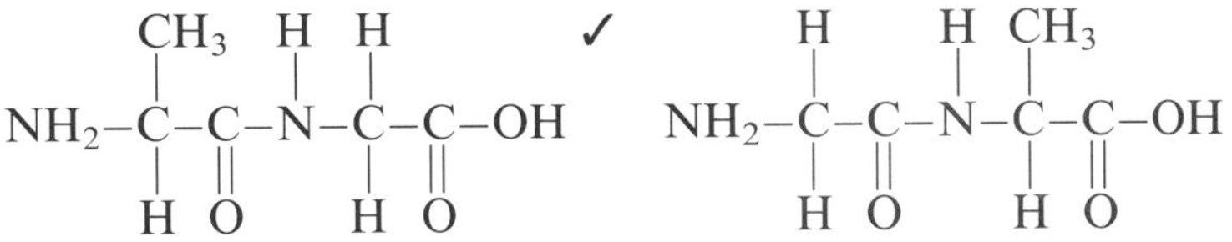

> **TIP**
>
> As a general rule put all the H-atoms in your structural formulae. You will usually lose marks if you leave them out. However, you should ignore the H-atoms when you are only working out the number of possible isomers of a hydrocarbon, especially if you are asked only for the number and their systematic names, and not their structures.

(d) <u>Reduction of Tollen's reagent</u> suggests that **A** contains an <u>aldehyde group</u> $–CHO$. ✓ So possible structures for **A** are $CH_3CH_2CH_2–CHO$ [butanal] and $(CH_3)_2CH–CHO$ [2-methylpropanal]. ✓ The probable structure for **B** is $CH_3CH_2COCH_3$ [butanone] ✓ which would be <u>reduced</u> ✓ by sodium tetrahydridoborate(III) to compound **C**, the secondary alcohol $CH_3CH_2CH(OH)CH_3$ [butan-2-ol] ✓ which has a <u>chiral centre</u> because there are <u>four different groups attached to a carbon</u> atom. ✓ **6 marks**

**Total: 17 marks**

**TIP**

Question 1(d) shows why you should consider all the clues before starting to write your answer. Examiners expect you to know test tube reactions to identify and distinguish between different functional groups. Make sure you remember the **reagents**, the **conditions** and the **observations** as well as understanding the organic reactions that take place.

**2.** (a)

 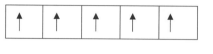 ✓

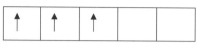 ✓

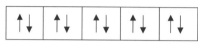 ✓ **3 marks**

**TIP**

Electrons occupy d-orbitals singly before pairing up. The 3d-level has a particular stability when all five orbitals are either half-filled $(3d^5)$ or completely filled $(3d^{10})$ as in Cr and Cu atoms respectively in the ground state. The 4s electrons are lost first when ions are formed. Candidates often lose marks on the electronic structures of transition metal atoms and ions.

   (b)   (i)   +2 ✓                                                           **1 mark**

          (ii)   tetrahedral ✓                                               **1 mark**

   (c)

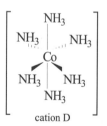

        cation A ✓               cation B ✓

        cation C ✓               cation D ✓          **4 marks**

**TIP**

Only aqueous chloride ions can give a precipitate with silver nitrate:

$$Ag^+(aq) + Cl^-(aq) \rightarrow AgCl(s)$$

Chlorine atoms attached as ligands to the central transition metal atom by strong covalent bonds cannot react with the aqueous silver cations unless the bonds break heterolytically.

   (d)   (i)   $[Cu(H_2O)_6]^{2+}$ ✓                                        **1 mark**

          (ii)   $[Cu(NH_3)_4(H_2O)_2]^{2+}$ ✓   octahedral ✓         **2 marks**

          (iii)   tetrachlorocuprate(II) ✓   $CuCl_4^{2-}$ ✓         **2 marks**

          (iv)   $2CuSO_4(aq) + 4KI(aq) \rightarrow Cu_2I_2(s) + 2K_2SO_4(aq) + I_2(aq)$ ✓    **1 mark**

                                                                **Total: 15 marks**

> **TIP**
>
> Watch out for the reaction in 2(d)(iv). It's a favourite with examiners.
> The copper cation is reduced from +2 to +1 and the iodide anion is oxidised from −1 to 0.
> The iodine can be titrated with aqueous sodium thiosulphate, $Na_2S_2O_3(aq)$ using starch as an indicator, so the reaction can be used quantitatively to estimate copper in copper(II) sulphate.

3. (a) The standard electrode potential of a metal is the <u>e.m.f. of a cell</u>, at a <u>standard temperature of 25 °C</u>, consisting of a half-cell of the metal in contact with its aqueous ions at a <u>concentration of 1.0 mol dm$^{-3}$</u> ✓ and a <u>standard hydrogen electrode</u> as the other half-cell. ✓  **2 marks**

> **TIP**
>
> Candidates often fail to score full marks on 3(a) because they omit one or more essential points from their definition. You can use your own words but make sure you include these five factors: the metal, the solution of its ions, the concentration of the metal ions, the temperature and the standard hydrogen electrode as the arbitrary reference. What a lot!

   (b) (i) agar jelly/filter paper with <u>saturated aqueous potassium chloride</u> ✓  **1 mark**

   (ii) $E_{Cu}^{\ominus} - E_{Zn}^{\ominus} = +0.34 - (-0.76) = +1.10\,V$ ✓  **1 mark**

   (iii) $Zn(s)\,|\,Zn^{2+}(aq)\,\vdots\vdots\,Cu^{2+}(aq)\,|\,Cu(s)$ ✓  **1 mark**

   (iv) $E_{Ag}^{\ominus} - E_{Cu}^{\ominus} = +0.46$ so $E_{Ag}^{\ominus} = +0.46 + (+0.34) = 0.80\,V$ ✓  **1 mark**

   (v) From the copper to the silver rod. ✓  **1 mark**

   (c) (i) <u>0.03 mol $I_2$(aq)</u> ✓ because $3 \times 2I^-$(aq) needed to give 6e$^-$ to $1 \times Cr_2O_7^{2-}$(aq)  **1 mark**

   (ii) The dioxovanadium(V) ion, $VO_2^+$(aq), ✓ <u>more readily accepts electrons</u> ($E^{\ominus}/V = 1.00$) to form oxovanadium(IV) ion, $VO^{2+}$(aq), <u>than iron(III) ions</u> accept electrons ($E^{\ominus}/V = 0.77$) to form iron(II) ions or <u>iodine molecules</u> accept electrons ($E^{\ominus}/V = 0.54$) to form iodide ions, so <u>iron(II) ions</u>, $Fe^{2+}$(aq) and <u>iodide ions</u>, $I^-$(aq) <u>could reduce dioxovanadium(V) ions to oxovanadium(IV) ions.</u> ✓  **2 marks**

> **TIP**
>
> $E^{\ominus}$ value does not change with amount of substance: e.g. $E^{\ominus} = +0.54\,V$ for $\frac{1}{2}I_2 + e^- \rightleftharpoons I^-$ and for $I_2 + 2e^- \rightleftharpoons 2I^-$ but $E^{\ominus}$ sign changes on reversing half-reaction direction: e.g. $E^{\ominus} = -0.54\,V$ for $I^- \rightleftharpoons \frac{1}{2}I_2 + e^-$. A reaction is feasilbe if $E^{\ominus}$ for the complete cell (two half-cells) is positive.

   (iii) When the drops of the aqueous potassium manganate(VII) come into contact with the aqueous vanadium(IV) sulphate, their <u>purple colour disappears</u> ✓ and the <u>blue solution turns greeny-blue then green</u> ✓ [when half the vanadium(IV) has changed into vanadium(V)] to yellowy-green then yellow [when all the vanadium(IV) has changed into vanadium(V)] and <u>finally pinky-yellow</u> ✓ [when a slight excess of manganate(VII) is added].  **3 marks**

   (iv) 1 mol $MnO_4^-$(aq) would oxidise 5 mol $Fe^{2+}$(aq) ✓ (from the table)

   ∴ 25.0 cm$^3$ of solution contains $5 \times (19.1 \times 0.00188/1000) = 1.80 \times 10^{-4}$ mol $Fe^{2+}$(aq) ✓

   ∴ 250 cm$^3$ of solution would contain $1.80 \times 10^{-3}$ mol Fe ✓

   Hence mass of iron in one tablet is $55.9 \times 1.80 \times 10^{-3} = 0.101\,g$ ✓  **4 marks**

   **Total: 17 marks**

**TIP**

You could get volumetric calculations in your written theory papers as well as in your practical assessments. Always make sure that any stoichiometric chemical equation is correct and properly balanced. Be consistent with the significant figures in your working and your final answer which should be given in the appropriate units.

**4.** (a)  (i)  rate $= k[NO(g)][Cl_2(g)]$ ✓                                                **1 mark**

(ii)  The sum of the <u>powers of the concentrations</u> of substances <u>in the rate equation</u> which for (a)(i) is $1+1=2$ (first order for NO, first order for $Cl_2$ and <u>second order overall</u>). ✓                                                          **1 mark**

**TIP**

Examiners always set questions on kinetics. Learn the definitions of *order* and *rate constant*. Make sure that you know how to obtain *order* and *rate constant* from experimental results and that you can work out the units for rate constants. Remember the rate equations can only be determined experimentally; they cannot be deduced from the stoichiometric equation.

(b)  (i)  $k = A\,e^{-E_a/RT}$

$E_a/RT$ is $(85\,000\,\mathrm{J\,mol^{-1}}) \div (8.31\,\mathrm{J\,K^{-1}\,mol^{-1}} \times 600\,\mathrm{K}) = 17.0$

$k$ is $(4.0 \times 10^9\,\mathrm{mol^{-1}\,dm^3\,s^{-1}}) \times \mathrm{e}^{-17.0} = 166\,\mathrm{mol^{-1}\,dm^3\,s^{-1}}$ ✓        **1 mark**

**TIP**

Remember that the $R$ is in $\mathrm{J\,K^{-1}\,mol^{-1}}$ so $E_a$ must be in $\mathrm{J\,mol^{-1}}$ (not $\mathrm{kJ\,mol^{-1}}$).
Save marks by watching the units to avoid this common mistake.
Watch significant figures and the units of $k$.
Make sure you can use the ln and $\mathrm{e}^x$ button on your calculator.

(ii)  $E_a$ is <u>minimum energy required for a reaction</u> to occur when the particles (atoms, molecules or ions) collide. <u>The higher the value of $E_a$</u>, the smaller the number of particles with enough energy, and so the <u>slower is the reaction</u>. ✓            **1 mark**

(c)  (i)  $Cl-Cl + NO \xrightarrow{\text{slow}} \overset{\text{transition state}\ ✓}{Cl\cdots Cl\cdots NO} \rightarrow Cl + Cl-NO$   **1 mark**

(ii)  The rate determining process is the <u>two molecules colliding</u> in <u>appropriate orientation</u> ✓ and with <u>enough energy</u> to <u>achieve the transition state</u>. ✓     **2 marks**

**TIP**

We use the experimental data to find which species could take part in the slowest (rate-determining) step. From this information we can suggest mechanisms but we usually need further and more detailed experimental work to confirm one particular mechanism. You should score marks for any sensible mechanism which fits the experimental data.

(d)  (i)  Monitor the <u>total pressure of the gaseous mixture</u> ✓ kept <u>at constant volume</u> because decomposition of <u>two moles of pentoxide yields five moles</u> of gaseous products, so the <u>pressure would increase with time</u> ✓ as the reaction proceeds.     **2 marks**

(ii)

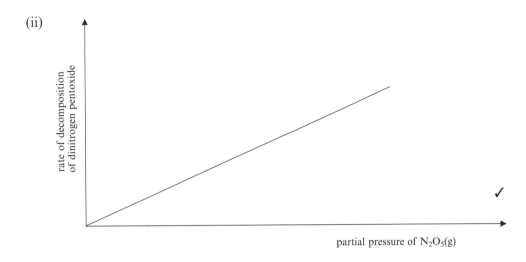

**1 mark**

> **TIP**
>
> If the rate $= k[X]^n$ then the graphs of rate vs [X] are as follows:
>
> $n = 0$      a straight line parallel to the [ ] axis;
>
> $n = 1$      a straight line through the origin of slope $k$;
>
> $n = 2$      part of a parabola through the origin.

(iii) For this first order reaction, rate $\propto$ [$N_2O_5(g)$] and for a gaseous mixture, partial pressure is directly proportional to the concentration, [$N_2O_5(g)$], so rate of decomposition of dinitrogen pentoxide $\propto$ partial pressure as shown by the above linear graph. ✓      **1 mark**

**Total: 11 marks**

# Paper 4 (Module) marking scheme

**1.** (a)   Brittle crystalline solids ✓ that can be cleaved and have high melting points ✓

**2 marks**

(b)   The heat change at constant pressure when one mole of an ionic compound is formed ✓ under standard conditions of T and P from its constituent gaseous ions. ✓   **2 marks**

> **TIP**
>
> You can define lattice enthalpy for the exothermic formation of the solid from its gaseous ions (so the value is negative) or for the endothermic conversion of the solid into its gaseous ions (so the value is positive). Check your syllabus to see which definition is used by your particular examination board.

(c)   The size of the ions ✓ and their charge. ✓   **2 marks**

(d)   $(+289) + (+732) + (+121) + (-364) + \Delta H_{lattice} = (-127)$

Hence, $\Delta H_{lattice} = (-127) - [(+289) + (+732) + (+121) + (-364)]$ ✓

$= -905 \, \text{kJ mol}^{-1}$ ✓ (✓ for correct sign and unit)   **3 marks**

> **TIP**
>
> Don't get confused and miss these easy marks. A Born–Haber cycle is just another example of Hess's law: the total enthalpy change is independent of the route taken. Start on the cycle at $Ag(s) + \frac{1}{2}Cl_2(g)$ and follow the arrows to $AgCl(s)$ clockwise (route 1 – five arrows) and anticlockwise (route 2 – one arrow). Write each term (value **and** sign) inside a bracket.

(e)   The bonding in the silver chloride lattice has some covalent character. ✓ The crystal is not the purely ionic compound, $Ag^+Cl^-(s)$, in calculating the theoretical value.   **1 mark**

**Total: 10 marks**

**2.** (a)

| Ion | Number of bonding pairs of electrons | Number of non-bonding pairs of electrons | Shape of ion |
|---|---|---|---|
| Nitronium, $NO_2^+$ | 4 | 4 | **Linear** |
| Chlorate(V), $ClO_3^-$ | 3 | 1 | Trigonal pyramidal |
| Hydronium, $H_3O^+$ | **3** | 1 | **Trigonal pyramidal** |
| Ammonium, $NH_4^+$ | **4** | 0 | **Tetrahedral** |
| | ✓ | ✓ | ✓   **3 marks** |

> **TIP**
>
> When you predict the shape of a molecule or ion, make sure you write about the repulsion between pairs of electrons (**not** atoms). You must work out the number of bonding (bb) **and** non-bonding (nb) pairs that repel one another as far apart as possible before you can predict their positions in space. Note the repulsion order between pairs is: nb : nb > nb : bb > bb : bb.

(b)   (i)   Fluorine is the most electronegative of all the elements, so the intermolecular forces in hydrogen fluoride consist of hydrogen bonding ✓ and permanent dipole–dipole attractions in addition to the weak van der Waals' attractive forces between the molecules of the other hydrogen halides. ✓   **2 marks**

(ii) The pairs of molecules are held together by <u>hydrogen bonding</u>. ✓

$$CH_3 - C \overset{\displaystyle O \cdots HO}{\underset{\displaystyle OH \cdots O}{}} C - CH$$ ✓

**2 marks**

> **TIP**
>
> A hydrogen bond ($\cdots$) is a weak bond between a very electronegative atom (X = F, O or N) and a hydrogen atom bonded to a very electronegative atom (Y = F, O or N), thus X$\cdots$Y. Examiners often set questions on hydrogen bonding to explain certain properties of ammonia, water, hydrogen fluoride, proteins and base pairing in the double helix of DNA.

(iii) <u>Hydrogen bonding</u> gives ice an <u>open crystal structure</u>. ✓ When the ice melts the <u>open structure collapses</u> and the resulting <u>decrease in volume</u> is accompanied by an <u>increase in density</u>. ✓  **2 marks**

(c) (i) The <u>cations and anions attract the polar water molecules</u> into the ionic lattice and become hydrated. ✓ The <u>water molecules diminish the electrostatic forces between the ions</u> so they can separate and disperse into the bulk of the water. ✓ The <u>energy given out by the hydration</u> of the ions <u>compensates for the energy taken in by the disruption of the crystal lattice</u>. ✓  **3 marks**

(ii) A salt dissolves in water <u>exothermically</u> if the <u>hydration energy released is greater than the lattice energy absorbed</u>. ✓ If the <u>hydration energy released is less than the lattice energy absorbed</u>, the salt dissolves <u>endothermically</u>. ✓  **2 marks**

(d) (i) interlocking <u>face-centred</u> cubes ✓ <u>cation coordination number $= 6$</u> ✓  **2 marks**

(ii) The <u>caesium cation</u> is <u>larger than</u> the <u>sodium cation</u> ✓ so caesium chloride forms an interlocking double simple cubic structure with the cation coordination number $= 8$.  **1 mark**

**Total: 17 marks**

> **TIP**
>
> Look at the space for the answer and at our mark scheme for 2(d)(ii). What a shame to get no mark for those structural details! Always be concise and answer the question set (**not** the one you wanted). Work out the length of answer from the space allocated and the number of points required in your answer from the marks allotted. Avoid those irrelevant answers!

**3.** (a) (i) **NaCl(aq)**

Addition of $AgNO_3$(aq): <u>white precipitate</u> forms ✓

Exposure to sunlight: <u>precipitate rapidly darkens/deep purple</u> ✓

Treatment with $NH_3$(aq): precipitate 'dissolves' to give a <u>colourless solution</u> ✓
**3 marks**

**NaBr(aq)**

Addition of $AgNO_3$(aq): <u>off-white/cream precipitate</u> forms ✓

Exposure to sunlight: <u>precipitate slowly darkens</u> ✓

Treatment with $NH_3$(aq): precipitate partially 'dissolves' ✓  **3 marks**

**NaI(aq)**

Addition of $AgNO_3$(aq): <u>pale yellow precipitate</u> forms ✓

Exposure to sunlight: <u>precipitate does not change colour</u> ✓

Treatment with $NH_3$(aq): <u>precipitate does not dissolve</u> ✓  **3 marks**

(ii) <u>No precipitate</u> would form because <u>silver fluoride is soluble in water</u> ✓  **1 mark**

(b)   $Cl_2(g) + 2NaOH(aq) \rightarrow NaCl(aq) + NaClO(aq) + H_2O(l)$ ✓ In a disproportionation reaction, the oxidation number of an element simultaneously increases and decreases. ✓ In this case $Cl(0) \rightarrow Cl(-1)$ in NaCl and $Cl(+1)$ in NaCO. ✓                    **3 marks**

(c)   Unlike the carbon atom, the silicon atom can extend its outer electron shell beyond eight. ✓ So the $SiCl_4$ can act as a Lewis acid with the Si atom accepting lone pairs of electrons from water molecules acting as a Lewis base. Subsequently, the SijCl bonds can break as the resulting products lose hydrogen chloride. ✓                    **2 marks**

**Total: 15 marks**

4. (a)   Sulphur vapour is burnt ✓$\frac{1}{2}$ to sulphur dioxide: $S(g) + O_2(g) \rightarrow SO_2(g)$ ✓$\frac{1}{2}$

The sulphur dioxide is converted to sulphur trioxide ✓$\frac{1}{2}$ by reaction with excess oxygen ✓$\frac{1}{2}$ from the air at a temperature of about 450 °C ✓$\frac{1}{2}$ and pressure just above atmospheric ✓$\frac{1}{2}$ with a heterogeneous catalyst ✓$\frac{1}{2}$ of promoted vanadium(V) oxide: ✓$\frac{1}{2}$

$2SO_2(g) + O_2(g) \rightleftharpoons 2SO_3(g)$ ✓$\frac{1}{2}$

The equilibrium percentage of sulphur trioxide in this exothermic reversible reaction would be favoured by a low temperature ✓$\frac{1}{2}$ and a high pressure. ✓$\frac{1}{2}$ The rate of attainment of equilibrium would be favoured by high temperature ✓$\frac{1}{2}$ and high pressure. ✓$\frac{1}{2}$ The percentage of $SO_3(g)$ in the equilibrium mixture is optimised using a catalyst and a compromise temperature. ✓$\frac{1}{2}$ A high pressure is not used ✓$\frac{1}{2}$ because the very slight increase in the equilibrium percentage of sulphur trioxide ✓$\frac{1}{2}$ does not justify the extra running costs. ✓$\frac{1}{2}$ The reacting gases are purified ✓$\frac{1}{2}$ to avoid poisoning the catalyst. ✓$\frac{1}{2}$

The sulphur trioxide is absorbed by 98% sulphuric acid ✓$\frac{1}{2}$ until the 2% water it contains is used up: ✓$\frac{1}{2}$

$SO_3(g) + H_2O(\text{in 98% sulphuric acid}) \rightarrow H_2SO_4(\text{100% sulphuric acid})$ ✓$\frac{1}{2}$

Some of the resulting 100% sulphuric acid is taken away as final product ✓$\frac{1}{2}$ and water is added to the rest to reform the 98% acid ✓$\frac{1}{2}$ used for absorbing the sulphur trioxide coming from the reaction vessel. The sulphur trioxide is not added directly to water because it would form a stable mist of sulphuric acid. ✓$\frac{1}{2}$

**any $12 \times$ ✓$\frac{1}{2}$ = maximum 6 marks**

(b) (i) $K_c = \dfrac{[CH_3CO_2C_2H_5]_{eqm}[H_2O]_{eqm}}{[CH_3CO_2H]_{eqm}[C_2H_5OH]_{eqm}}$ ✓

1 mol $CH_3COOH$ reacts with 1 mol $C_2H_5OH$ to give 1 mol $CH_3COOC_2H_5$ and 1 mol $H_2O$.

So if at equilibrium the ratio of ester to acid is $2:1$ then the ratio of water to acid is $2:1$. ✓

Since equal amounts of acid and alcohol were mixed initially then the ratio of ester to alcohol and of water to alcohol must also be $2:1$. ✓

Hence, the value of $K_c$ is $(2/1) \times (2/1) = 4$ ✓

**4 marks**

**TIP**

Remember that for $K_c$ the concentrations must be the equilibrium values. First write the stoichiometric chemical equation. Next write the initial concentrations. Finally write the concentrations at equilibrium. You will usually have to find the $K_c$ value (and its units, if any) or an unknown equilibrium concentration of a specified component.

(ii) **I** – the percentage of ethanol converted to ester would <u>decrease</u> ✓ because <u>$K_c$ for exothermic reactions decreases with increasing temperature</u>. ✓

**II** – the rate at which equilibrium is established would <u>increase</u> ✓ because the <u>numbers of molecules having the minimum energy</u> needed to react (the activation energy, $E_a$) <u>increase with increasing temperature</u>. ✓

**4 marks**

(c) (i) <u>Homogeneous</u> catalysts are in the <u>same phase as the reactants</u>. <u>Heterogeneous</u> catalysts are in a <u>different phase</u> from the reactants. ✓

**1 mark**

**TIP**

Make sure you are familiar with the heterogeneous catalysts commonly used in important industrial processes: Fe in the Haber synthesis of $NH_3$; $V_2O_5$ in the Contact process for $H_2SO_4$; Pt/Rh in the oxidation of $NH_3$ to manufacture $HNO_3$; Ni in the hydrogenation of oil to fat to produce margarine; $H_3PO_4$ on silica in the direct hydration of ethene gas.

(ii)

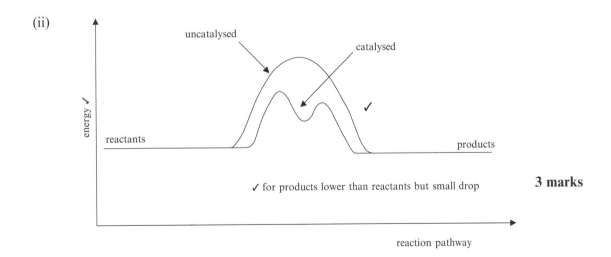

✓ for products lower than reactants but small drop

**3 marks**

**Total: 18 marks**

**TIP**

You could label the vertical axis energy, enthalpy, E or H. The horizontal axis could be reaction coordinate or pathway. Do **not** label the vertical axis $\Delta E$ or $\Delta H$. The horizontal axis should **never** be labelled time or temperature. Note that the products line is below the reactants line and the difference is small: $\Delta H$ for the exothermic reaction is $-2\,kJ\,mol^{-1}$.

# Paper 5 (Synoptic) marking scheme

## Section A

**1.** (a)  (i)

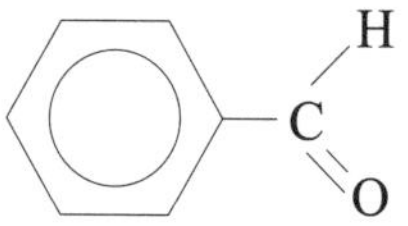

✓

         **1 mark**

    (ii)  $C_6H_5CHCl_2 + H_2O \rightarrow C_6H_5CHO + 2HCl$ ✓    **1 mark**

    (iii)  $C_6H_5CO_2H$ ✓    **1 mark**

  (b)  (i)  <u>geometrical</u> isomerism ✓    **1 mark**

    (ii)  **I** – A <u>black precipitate</u> or a <u>mirror of silver</u> is formed ✓

       **II** – the solution turns from <u>red-brown or orange to colourless</u> ✓    **2 marks**

    (iii)

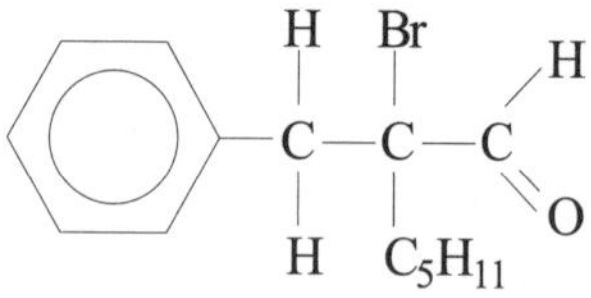

      ✓ for addition of HBr across double bond

      ✓ for correct orientation

                           **2 marks**

> **TIP**
>
> Answer 1(b)(iii) shows that during electrophilic addition of HBr across the double bond of an unsymmetrical alkene the bromine will attach to the carbon atom with the fewer number of H-atoms. This is Markovnikow's rule which relates to the stabilities of possible carbocation intermediates. In UV light, H· and ·Br free radicals add to either carbon atom.

  (c)  (i)

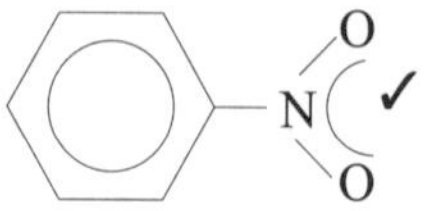

**A** nitrobenzene 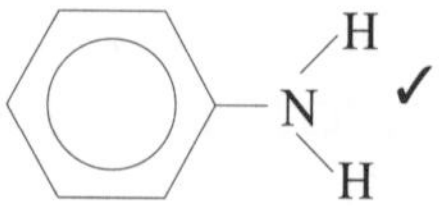      **B** phenylamine 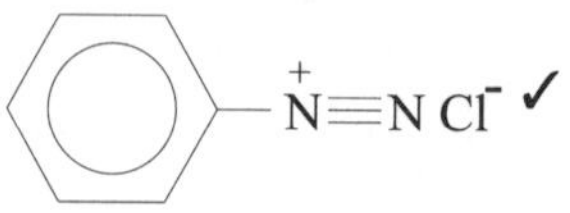      **C** benzenediazonium chloride

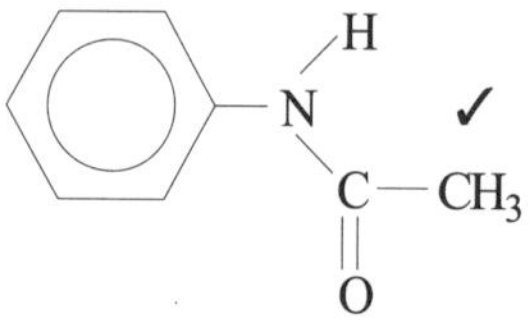

                                      **5 marks**

**D** N-phenylethanamide 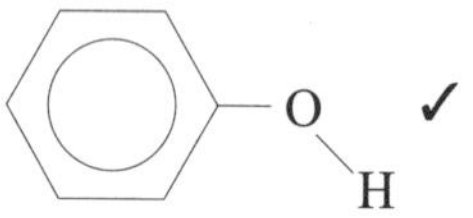      **E** phenol

    (For each mark the candidate must have an unambiguous structure **and** the correct name.)

    (ii)

2,4,6-tribromophenol  

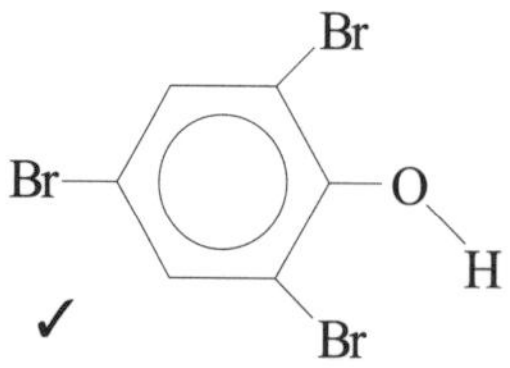

       ✓          ✓

                                        **2 marks**

                                      **Total: 15 marks**

**2.** (a)  (i)  Brønsted–Lowry: an <u>acid is a proton donor</u> and a <u>base is a proton acceptor</u>. ✓

                                      **1 mark**

    (ii)  Lewis: an <u>acid is an electron-pair acceptor</u> and a <u>base is an electron-pair donor</u>. ✓

                                        **1 mark**

(b)

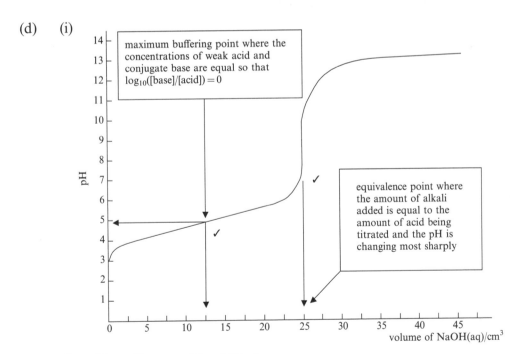

CH$_3$—Cl AlCl$_3$ ⟶ $\overset{+}{C}H_3$ + $\overset{-}{C}l$—AlCl$_3$

formation of the electrophile ✓ and the Wheland intermediate ✓ elimination of the proton leading to the product ✓

**3 marks**

(c)  (i)  A solution of a weak acid and its conjugate base (or a weak base and its conjugate acid) whose pH is almost unchanged by the addition of small amounts of acid or alkali. ✓   **1 mark**

(ii)  $pK_a = -\log_{10}(K_a/\text{mol dm}^{-3})$ so $pK_a$ is $(-\log_{10}(1.4 \times 10^{-5}) = 4.85$

$pH = pK_a + \log_{10}([\text{salt}]/[\text{acid}])$ so $5.2 = 4.85 + \log_{10}([\text{salt}]/0.18)$

∴ $\log_{10}([\text{salt}]/0.18) = 0.35$ so $[\text{salt}]/0.18 = 2.24$

∴ $[\text{salt}] = 0.403\ \text{mol dm}^{-3}$ ✓

molar mass of sodium propanoate is

$2 \times 12.0 + 5 \times 1.0 + 12.0 + 2 \times 16.0 + 1.0 + 23.0 = 96.0\ \text{g mol}^{-1}$ ✓

∴ mass of salt is $96.0\ \text{g mol}^{-1} \times 0.403\ \text{mol dm}^{-1} = 39\ \text{g}$ ✓   **3 marks**

**TIP**

Show your working in calculations and give your final answer to the appropriate significant figures. In 2(c)(ii) we use the data as given but round our final answer from 38.7 to 39 because our accuracy is limited by the acid concentration and pH given to two significant figures (0.18 and 5.2). Examiners detest the 8- or 10-digit figures copied from calculators!

(d)  (i)

maximum buffering point where the concentrations of weak acid and conjugate base are equal so that $\log_{10}([\text{base}]/[\text{acid}]) = 0$

equivalence point where the amount of alkali added is equal to the amount of acid being titrated and the pH is changing most sharply

*(graph: pH vs volume of NaOH(aq)/cm$^3$, with ✓ marks)*

**2 marks**

(ii)  $pH = pK_a$ ✓ so $pH = 4.87$ ✓   **2 marks**

(iii)  phenolphthalein ✓ because it <u>changes</u> from colourless to pink <u>in the range from 8.0 to 10.0</u> at the equivalence point <u>where the pH titration curve is steepest.</u> ✓

**2 marks**

**Total: 15 marks**

**3.** (a) (i) The amphoteric aluminium oxide dissolves in the sodium hydroxide to form a solution of sodium aluminate ✓ and the other insoluble metal (hydr)oxides impurities can be removed by filtration. ✓
**2 marks**

(ii) $2Al(OH)_3 \rightarrow Al_2O_3 + 3H_2O$ ✓
**1 mark**

(iii) $(Na^+)_3[AlF_6]^{3-}$ ✓ octahedral ✓
**2 marks**

(iv) $27\,000\,kg$ of aluminium contains $1 \times 10^6\,mol\ Al = 6.02 \times 10^{29}$ atoms ✓

The charge on an $Al^{3+}$ ion is $3 \times 1.60 \times 10^{-19} = 4.80 \times 10^{-19}$ C

So the quantity of electricity required to produce 27 tonnes of aluminium is

$4.80 \times 10^{-19} \times 6.02 \times 10^{29} = 2.89 \times 10^{11}$ C ✓
**2 marks**

(v) The price of aluminium depends very strongly on the cost of the large amount of electricity required for its extraction. ✓
**1 mark**

(vi) Aluminium is a strong but low density metal, so it is alloyed with magnesium, a similar metal, to form tough but lightweight metals used widely in the aircraft industry. ✓
**1 mark**

(b) (i) $TiO_2 + 2C + 2Cl_2 \rightarrow TiCl_4 + 2CO$ ✓ (allow $TiO_2 + C + 2Cl_2 \rightarrow TiCl_4 + CO_2$)
**1 mark**

(ii) The sodium metal used in the extraction of titanium must itself be manufactured by a rather expensive electrolytic extraction process ✓ from sodium chloride.
**1 mark**

(c) (i) As Ziegler–Natta stereospecific catalysts.
**1 mark**

(ii) Water hydrolyses this covalent chloride ✓ to titanium(IV) oxide and hydrochloric acid.
**1 mark**

(iii) Aluminium uses its 3 valence electrons to form a single covalent bond with each of three ethyl groups and achieve 6 electrons in its valence shell. ✓ Hence the Al atom in $Al(C_2H_5)_3$ can act as an electron-pair acceptor ✓ to achieve 8 electrons in its outer shell.
**2 marks**

**Total: 15 marks**

**4.** (a) (i) Terylene ✓ (any other valid example)
✓
**2 marks**

(ii) Silk ✓ (any other valid example)   $-\overset{\displaystyle O}{\underset{\displaystyle }{C}}-\overset{\displaystyle }{\underset{\displaystyle H}{N}}-$   ✓
**2 marks**

(b) (i) The even splitting of a single bond ✓ between two atoms sharing a pair of electrons so that each atom retains one electron. ✓ **2 marks**

(ii) An atom in the free radical has an unpaired electron. ✓ **1 mark**

(iii) $C_6H_5.CO.O.O.CO.C_6H_5 \rightarrow 2C_6H_5.CO.O$ ✓ **1 mark**

**TIP**

Free radicals form when the single covalent bond between the two oxygen atoms undergoes homolytic fission: $C_6H_5.CO.O-O.CO.C_6H_5 \rightarrow 2C_6H_5.CO.O\cdot$. Remember that · represents an unpaired electron. The bond between the oxygen atoms in an $O_2$ molecule is about $3\frac{1}{2}$ times stronger than that between two oxygen atoms in a peroxide like $H_2O_2$.

(c) (i)

✓ **1 mark**

(ii) Can be drawn into a flexible fibre because rotation about the single bonds in the $-(CH_2)_4-$ and $-(CH_2)_6-$ groups result in flexible linkages between the $-NH-CO-$ groups. ✓ **1 mark**

(iii)

✓

The polyamide will be more rigid ✓ because the aromatic ring between the $-NH-CO-$ groups lacks the flexibility of alkyl chains in Nylon-6,6. ✓ **3 marks**

(d) They may be non-biodegradable and pollute the environment. ✓ They are usually manufactured from valuable non-renewable fossil fuels. ✓ **2 marks**

**Total: 15 marks**

## Section B

**TIP**

If you have a comprehension exercise in your exam (check your syllabus), you will have to extract information from the given passage and also apply your grasp of chemistry to subject matter in the passage. Time is important, so read as quickly as possible but never sacrifice understanding for the sake of speed. It may help if you glance through the questions first.

5. (a) Citric acid is biodegradable so less likely to pollute the environment. ✓ EDTA is more efficient so less is required which makes it cheaper. ✓ **2 marks**

(b)

✓

The $-OH$ and $-CO_2H$ groups have at least one oxygen atom each with a lone pair of electrons available for dative bonding. ✓ Since the ligand forms only two (not four) dative bonds, the shape of its molecular structure presumably allows only two of these groups to be in the correct position at any one time to form a bond with the cation being complexed. ✓ **3 marks**

(c)  Six. ✓ Four ✓ if the nitrogen atom and one oxygen atom in each of the three jCO$_2$H groups in the ligand formed a dative bond with the cation being complexed. ✓

**3 marks**

(d)  Dative covalent (or coordinate) ✓ A nitrogen or oxygen atom donates a lone pair of electrons ✓ into an empty orbital of the metal cation. ✓  **3 marks**

(e)  Water ✓ carbon dioxide ✓ (or nitrogen oxides ✓). Any increase in the very small percentage of carbon dioxide in the atmosphere could enhance the 'greenhouse effect' and global warming. ✓ (or nitrogen oxides could cause 'acid rain' ✓)

**maximum 3 marks**

(f)  2− ✓ (because the EDTA anion is 4$^-$ and the calcium cation is 2$^+$).  **1 mark**

(g)  One mole of EDTA$^{4-}$(aq) will complex one mole of Ca$^{2+}$(aq). ✓

100 cm$^3$ of the solution contains $(100/1000) \times 1.00 \times 10^{-4} = 1.00 \times 10^{-5}$ mol  EDTA$^{4-}$ ✓

Molar mass of calcium, Ca$^{2+}$ is 40.0 g mol$^{-1}$

Hence maximum mass of calcium that could be removed is $40.0$ g mol$^{-1} \times 1.00 \times 10^{-5}$ $=1.00 \times 10^{-4}$ g. ✓  **3 marks**

(h)

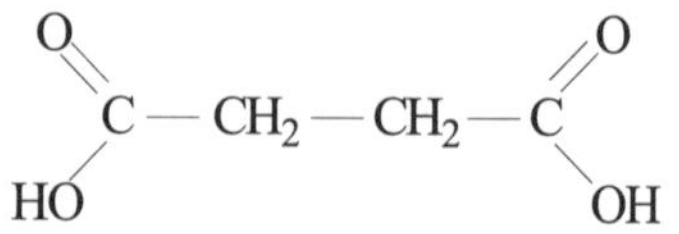

✓     butanedioic acid ✓                    **2 marks**

(i)  The −CO$_2$H(aq) will have ionised to −CO$_2^-$(aq) ✓ so making the oxygen atoms more powerful electron-pair donors. ✓  **2 marks**

(j)

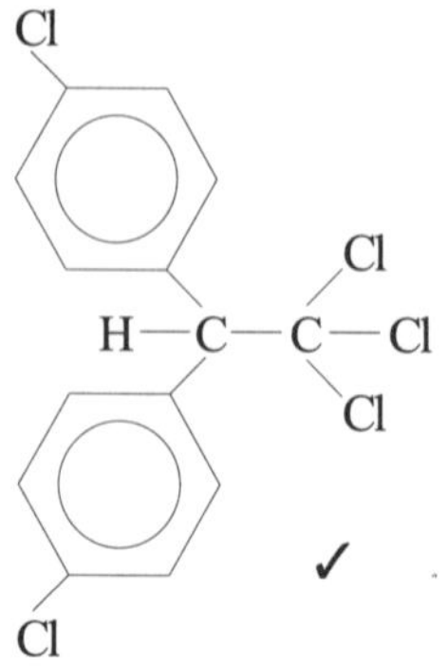

The molecule has little or no polarity ✓ and it is much larger than a water molecule. ✓ It has no groups capable of ionising in water ✓ and it has no nitrogen, oxygen or fluorine atoms capable of forming hydrogen bonds with water. ✓ [one ✓ only]

So DDT would be insoluble in water. ✓           **3 marks**

**Total: 25 marks**

**End of Paper 5**